UNIT 13: ALTERNATING CURRENT

CONTENTS

THE OPEN UNIVERSITY

A SECOND LEVEL COURSE

PREPARED BY THE COURSE TEAM

281: BASIC PHYSICAL SCIENCE FOR TECHNOLOGY

UNIT 13: ALTERNATING CURRENT
UNIT 14: ELECTRICAL INSTRUMENTS

THE OPEN UNIVERSITY PRESS

BASIC PHYSICAL SCIENCE FOR TECHNOLOGY

Course Team

I. Boustead	(Chairman)	E. Murphy	(Technology)
P. F. Chapman	(Technology)	J. M. Richards	(Technology)
R. M. Hardman	(Designer)	J. N. Siddall	(Graphic artist)
D. A. Johnson	(Science)	J. J. Sparkes	(Technology)
A. C. Jones	(Editor)	R. Steadman	(Assessor)
S. Lewis	(Designer)	G. M. Viggars	(Course co-ordinator)
R. S. Mackintosh	(Science)	G. Wexler	(Technology)
A. Millington	(BBC)	W. Young	(BBC)

Cover illustration: *The Pancake Making Machine* by W. Heath Robinson. © Estate of Mrs J. C. Heath Robinson/Penguin books.

The Open University Press
Walton Hall, Milton Keynes, MK7 6AA

First published 1984.

Designed by the Graphic Design Group of the Open University.

Filmset by Composition House Limited, Salisbury, Wiltshire.

Printed in Great Britain by Thamesdown Litho Limited, Swindon, Wiltshire.

ISBN 0 335 17165 6

This text forms part of an Open University course. A complete list of the units of the course appears at the end of this text.

For general availability of supporting material referred to in this text please write to: Open University Educational Enterprises Ltd., 12 Cofferidge Close, Stony Stratford, Milton Keynes MK11 1BY.

Further information on Open University Courses may be obtained from: The Admissions Office, The Open University, PO Box 48, Walton Hall, Milton Keynes, MK7 6AB.

1.1

Aims

The aim of this unit is to describe quantitatively the response of circuit components such as inductors, capacitors and resistors, individually and together, in a.c. circuits.

Objectives

After studying this unit you should be able to do the following:

1 Define, describe or otherwise explain the terms listed in Table A.

2 Describe a sinusoidal waveform by a mathematical equation, given the appropriate data.

3 Describe the response of a resistance to an instantaneous sinusoidal voltage.

4 Calculate r.m.s. values of current, voltage and power given the appropriate data.

5 Describe the response of a lossless inductor to an a.c. voltage.

6 Describe the response of a lossless capacitor to an a.c. voltage.

7 Calculate the impedance of individual circuit elements.

8 Calculate the impedance of two or more circuit elements in series in an a.c. circuit using phasor diagrams.

9 Calculate the impedance of two or more circuit elements in parallel in an a.c. circuit using admittance phasor diagrams.

10 Calculate power factor, given the appropriate data.

Table A Terms introduced in this unit

alternating current and voltage	phase difference
admittance	phasor
amplitude	phasor diagram
angular frequency	power factor
average power	power factor correction
d.c. current and voltage	reactor
displacement current	reactive device
frequency	resonance
hertz	resonance frequency
impedance	r.m.s. current, power, voltage
instantaneous voltage	sinusoidal waveform
parallelogram of phasors	varying d.c. current and voltage
peak voltage	

1 INTRODUCTION

In this unit we shall be looking at the behaviour of inductances, capacitances and resistances, singly and together, when supplied with an alternating current or voltage. An understanding of the way these components behave is vital for anyone wishing to understand the behaviour of even relatively simple circuits or devices designed to carry alternating or fluctuating currents and voltages (e.g. a motor, loudspeaker, radio set, etc.).

As usual the main components of this week's work are this unit text and the relevant questions in the *Problem Book*. You should work through this text, attempting the self-assessment questions as you come to them, and you will be referred to the *Problem Book* at the appropriate points as usual.

Many of the ideas in this unit may well be completely new to you and you could well find that your progress is somewhat slower than usual. However you will find that Unit 14 is very short so you can take about $1\frac{1}{2}$ weeks of study time over this unit if you wish.

2 WAVEFORMS OF CURRENT AND VOLTAGE

2.1 A.c and d.c.

If a battery is connected across a resistor, the voltage drop across the resistor and the current flowing through it will not vary much with time. So a graph of current or voltage as a function of time will appear as in Figure 1(a). Such constant currents are usually referred to as direct currents or more simply, *d.c. currents* and the corresponding voltages are referred to as *d.c. voltages.*

If a battery is connected across a resistive device, such as a telephone microphone, whose resistance varies with time, the current still flows in the same direction at all times but is of varying magnitude, and might be as shown in Figure 1(b). Such currents are referred to as *varying d.c. currents.*

varying d.c. currents

If, however, a resistor were connected across the output of a sinusoidal voltage generator, such as that described in Unit 12, the voltage and current would appear as in Figure 1(c). Now the current and voltage vary not only in magnitude but also in direction. Such a current is called an *alternating current* or more simply an *a.c. current* and the corresponding voltage is called an *a.c. voltage.*

a.c. current **a.c. voltage**

The essential feature of an alternating current or voltage is that it repeatedly changes direction, unlike the varying direct current or voltage, where the magnitude changes but the direction does not. In practice, the terms 'a.c. voltage' and 'a.c. current' normally refer to sinusoidal waveforms (see next section), although many other alternating waveforms are possible.

The terms 'a.c.' is, of course, an abbreviation for alternating current. The corresponding abbreviation 'a.v.' for alternating voltage has never been widely used, and in the absence of a convenient abbreviation the usage 'a.c. voltage' has appeared. Furthermore, the term 'a.c.' is invariably used as an adjective (a.c. motor, a.c. circuit, etc.), so that when it is the alternating current itself that is being referred to, it is virtually never called 'an a.c.' Hence the apparent illogicality 'a.c. current'. Here, as elsewhere in the language, usage and logic are not in close agreement.

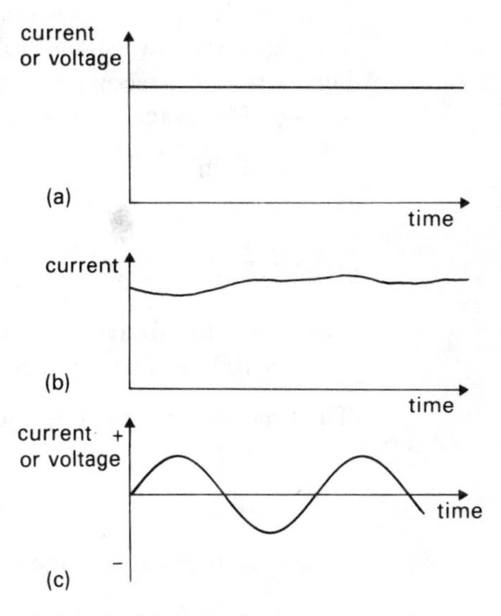

Figure 1 (a) DC voltage or current. (b) Varying d.c. current. (c) AC voltage or current

2.2 Sinusoidal waveforms

Electronics is concerned with a.c. voltages, which display a variety of waveforms. Figure 2 for example shows four different waveforms. Figure 2(a) represents a typical sawtooth wave of the type that might be applied to the deflection coils of a television tube; the gradual rise in voltage V causes the electron beam to scan across the screen and the sudden change causes it to fly back. Figure 2(b), a digital waveform, is the kind of waveform used to carry

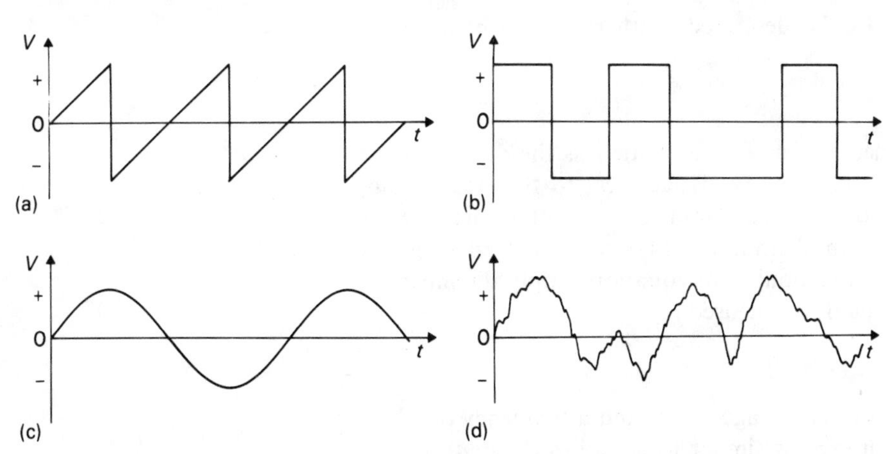

Figure 2 Different waveforms that might be encountered in electronic circuits

data in computers or modern communications systems. Figure 2(c) is a *sinusoidal waveform*. Figure 2(d) shows the kind of waveform produced by speech or random noise. It is not periodic; that is, it does not have a repeating pattern.

sinusoidal waveform

Most common electrical circuits, whatever waveforms they are handling, can be analysed in terms of either their response to sinusoidal waveforms of various frequencies or their response to step functions (i.e. off–on or on–off switching). This latter type of response was introduced in Unit 12 when we considered what happens when an inductor is switched on. This unit, however, concentrates on the properties of sinusoidal waveforms and the effects of circuit elements on them.

For a sinusoidal voltage, the voltage at an instant, v, is related to time t by an equation of the form

$$v = V_{\text{m}} \sin \omega t, \tag{1}$$

where V_{m} and ω are constants. Graphically such a voltage is as shown by the solid curve in Figure 3. The parameter v is referred to as the *instantaneous voltage* and quantity V_{m} is the *peak voltage* or *amplitude*.

instantaneous voltage
peak voltage **amplitude**

The constant ω is known as the *angular frequency* and is measured in radians per second. You will recall that when we discussed the generator in Unit 12, angular frequency was first introduced as a means of describing the angular velocity of the coil as it turned in the magnetic field.

angular frequency

Rather then thinking of *angular* frequency you may be more accustomed to thinking of *frequency*, measured in cycles per second (that is, *hertz*). However, one complete cycle corresponds to an angle of 2π radians (or 360°), so a frequency of f hertz (cycles per second) corresponds to an angular frequency of $2\pi f$ radians per second. This is the angular frequency ω. Hence

frequency **hertz**

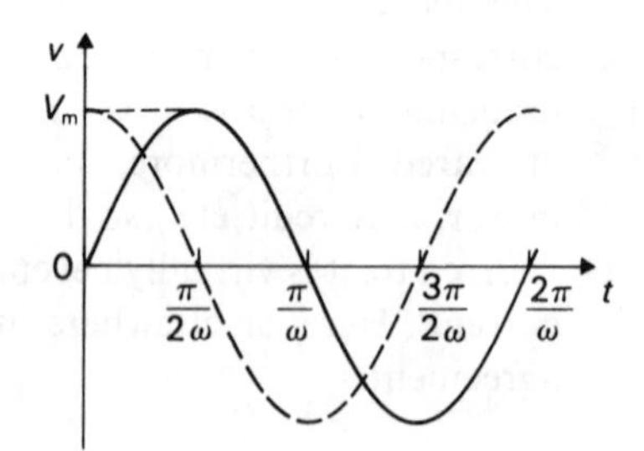

Figure 3 Instantaneous voltage v as a function of time t for a sinusoidal voltage of the form $v = V_{\text{m}} \sin \omega t$. (solid curve) and $v = V_{\text{m}} \cos \omega t$ (broken curve)

$$\omega = 2\pi f$$

or

$$f = \frac{\omega}{2\pi}. \tag{2}$$

Thus the mains frequency of 50 hertz corresponds to an angular frequency of $2\pi \times 50 = 100\pi$ radians per second.

The time to complete one cycle is simply

$$\frac{1}{\text{Frequency}},$$

or $1/f$, so the time for one cycle is

$$\frac{1}{f} = \frac{2\pi}{\omega}. \tag{3}$$

A sinusoidal waveform can also be described mathematically by a cosine function. For example,

$$v = V_{\text{m}} \cos \omega t,$$

where the symbols are as defined earlier. This is plotted as the dashed line in Figure 3. Notice that the *shape* of the wave is identical to that for the sine function. The only difference is that it is displaced relative to the sine function on the time axis. In calculations on alternating voltages and currents we may use either the sine or the cosine function; both equations apply to sinusoidal waveforms. (The term 'cosinusoidal' is not used.)

SAQ 1 (Objective 2)

A sinusoidal voltage has a peak voltage of 5 V and a frequency of 1 kHz (10^3 hertz). Write down an express similar to equation (1) for this wave form.

SAQ 2 (Objective 2)

A sinusoidal current i has a peak value of 2 A and a frequency of 100 Hz. Calculate:

(a) the time for one cycle of the current;

(b) the angular frequency in radians per second;

(c) the equation of the instantaneous current i if $i = 0$ when $t = 0$.

2.3 Phase difference

Sinusoids may differ from each other not only in amplitude (V_m) and angular frequency (ω) but also in phase; that is, sinusoids of the same frequency may differ in their position relative to each other on the time axis.

Look at Figure 4. This shows two sinusoidal wave forms A and B, with the same amplitude and the same frequency. (Note, the graphs have been plotted using ωt instead of t; this makes the units on the x-axis radians rather than seconds.) The difference between these two waveforms is that they are displaced relative to each other on the ωt axis. So let us write

$$v_A = V_m \sin \omega t \tag{4}$$

as the instantaneous voltage of curve A, and let us regard this as our reference waveform. It is clear from Figure 4 that curve B is lagging behind curve A; for example, curve A has passed through its maximum value and reached zero before curve B reaches its maximum value.

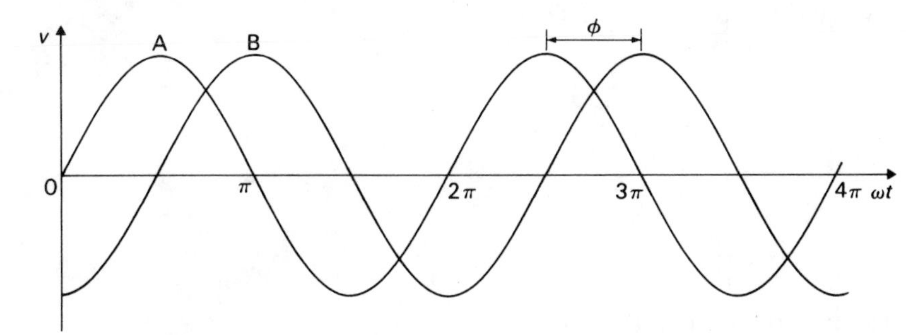

Figure 4 Instantaneous voltage v as a function of ωt for two sinusoids which exhibit a phase difference of ϕ

We can describe this difference quantitatively by defining a *phase difference* ϕ, which is measured in radians, such that the equation for curve B will be

phase difference

$$v_B = V_m \sin(\omega t - \phi). \tag{5}$$

This phase difference can be read directly from the graph, as shown in Figure 4.

On the other hand, curve B could be taken as the reference. The equation for curve B is

$$v_B = -V_m \cos \omega t. \tag{6}$$

The minus sign is necessary because $v_B = -V_m$ when $t = 0$, and $\cos \omega t = +1$ when $t = 0$. But curve A clearly *leads* curve B (i.e. A reaches a maximum before B) so we can describe A as having a *phase lead* of $+\phi$ over curve B. So

$$v_A = -V_m \cos(\omega t + \phi). \tag{7}$$

Note that ϕ, the phase difference in equations (4) to (7), is expressed as an angle in radians.

But what is the relationship between *time* lag or lead t_d of one sinusoid relative to another and the phase difference ϕ between them?

Let the two sinusoids be expressed as

$$v_1 = V_m \sin \omega t \tag{8}$$

and

$$v_2 = V_m \sin(\omega t - \phi). \tag{9}$$

We know their phase difference is ϕ, but what is the time lag of the second with respect to the first?

We know that $v_1 = 0$ when $t = 0$. So if we can find the moment when $v_2 = 0$, this must be the instant when $t = t_d$. The time t tells us the time interval between the same parts of the two waveforms.

Now, $v_2 = 0$ when $V_m \sin(\omega t_d - \phi) = 0$. That is, when $(\omega t_d - \phi) = 0$. So

$$\phi = \omega t_d$$

or

$$t_d = \frac{\phi}{\omega}. \tag{10}$$

Thus, for example, if the reference voltage is given by

$$v_1 = 5 \sin 10\pi t \text{ volts,}$$

and another sinusoidal voltage, given by

$$v_2 = 5 \sin(10\pi t - \phi) \text{ volts,}$$

lags behind it by 1 millisecond, what is the angle of phase lag?

Here $\omega = 10\pi$ and $t_d = 10^{-3}$ s. So, by equation (10), $\phi = \omega t_d$. Thus

$$\begin{aligned}\phi &= (10\pi \times 10^{-3}) \text{ radians}\\ &= 10^{-2}\pi \text{ radians.}\end{aligned}$$

Hence equation (9) becomes

$$v_2 = 5 \sin(10\pi t - 10^{-2}\pi) \text{ volts.}$$

SAQ 3 (Objective 2)

If a voltage sinusoid lags behind a current sinusoid of the same frequency by 5 milliseconds, what is their phase difference if the equation for current is given by $i = I_m \sin 1000t$?

SAQ 4 (Objective 2)

The output from a three-phase mains generator consists of three separate voltage sinusoids with an amplitude of 350 V and a frequency of 50 Hz. The windings on the generator from which these voltages are obtained are uniformly spaced around the stator. Write down the three equations which describe the instantaneous voltages of the three phases. (Remember that one complete cycle of a sinusoidal waveform corresponds to a phase change of 360° or 2π radians.)

2.4 Average value of a sinusoidal current

If a current i flows for a time t, the average current $i_{av.}$ during this period is given by

$$i_{av.} = \frac{\int_0^t i \, dt}{t}. \tag{11}$$

For sinusoidal waveforms, the average is taken over one complete cycle since the average over n cycles will be the same as the average over 1 cycle.

For a current represented by the equation

$$i = I_m \sin \omega t, \tag{12}$$

the average is found by considering time $t = 0$ to time $t = 2\pi/\omega$. Equation (11) becomes

$$i_{av.} = \frac{\int_0^{2\pi/\omega} I_m \sin \omega t \, dt}{2\pi/\omega}. \tag{13}$$

The integral of $\sin \omega t$ is $(\cos \omega t)/\omega$ (plus a constant), so equation (13) becomes

$$i_{av.} = \frac{I_m}{2\pi} [-\cos \omega t]_0^{2\pi/\omega}$$

$$= \frac{I_m}{2\pi} (-1 + 1)$$

$$= 0.$$

Thus the average current is zero. The reason for this can be seen in Figure 5. This shows the graph of one cycle of the sinusoid and the integral of the graph with respect to time is the area between the waveform and the time-axis; that is, the sum of the two shaded areas A and B in Figure 5. But the positive area A above

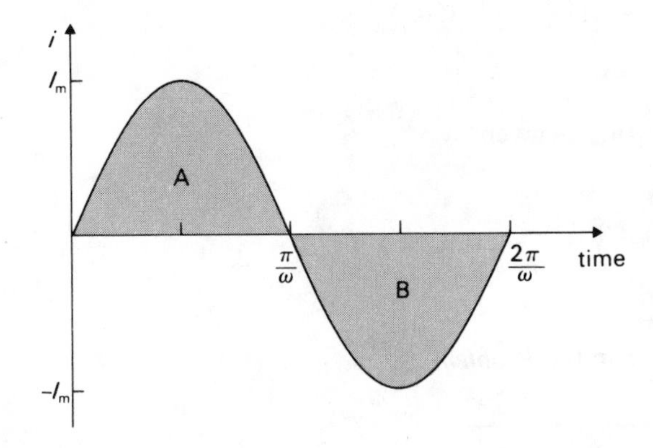

Figure 5 For a sinusoidal current $i = I_m \sin \omega t$, the integral under the curve is the sum of the positive area A and the negative area B; hence the average over one complete cycle is zero

the axis is equal to the negative area B below the axis, so the total area is zero, and so is the average value. That is, the electrons in a conductor carrying an alternating current oscillate, but their mean position, on average, does not alter. However, as you will see later, although the average current is zero, the power delivered is not zero, because power depends on i^2, which is always positive, even when i is negative.

2.5 Summary of section 2

1. In a sinusoidal a.c. voltage, the instantaneous voltage v varies with time t according to equations of the form

$$v = V_m \sin \omega t \quad \text{or} \quad v = V_m \cos \omega t,$$

where

V_m = peak voltage or amplitude,

ω = angular frequency.

2. Angular frequency ω in radians per second is related to frequency f in hertz (cycles per second) by the equation

$$\omega = 2\pi f.$$

3. When two sinusoids of the same frequency are displaced in time, the displacement can be expressed as a phase difference ϕ. Thus if the reference voltage has the equation

$$v = V_m \sin \omega t$$

the equation of a voltage lagging by a phase difference ϕ is

$$v_1 = V_m \sin(\omega t - \phi),$$

where ϕ is measured in radians.

4. The time delay t_d between two sinusoids which have a phase difference ϕ is given by

$$\phi = \omega t_d.$$

5. If a current i flows for a time t, the average current $i_{av.}$ is given by

$$i_{av.} = \frac{\int_0^t i \, dt}{t}$$

If $i = I_m \sin \omega t$, then $i_{av.}$ is zero.

You should now be able to attempt questions 521–5 in the *Problem Book.*

---

3 THE RESPONSE OF CIRCUIT COMPONENTS TO AC INPUTS

3.1 The response of resistors

If an alternating voltage v is applied to a resistor of resistance R a current i flows, and these parameters are related by the same equation as that used for d.c. circuits, that is

$$i = \frac{v}{R}, \tag{14}$$

where i and v are the instantaneous values of current and voltage respectively. So if $v = V_m \sin \omega t$, then

$$i = \frac{V_m}{R} \sin \omega t.$$

Thus the current reaches the maximum value of V_m/R at the same time as the applied voltage reaches its maximum value.

The power p dissipated in the resistor at any instant is given by the same equation as for d.c. circuits; that is

$$p = iv \tag{15}$$

$$= \frac{V_m}{R} \sin \omega t \times V_m \sin \omega t$$

$$= \frac{V_m^2}{R} \sin^2 \omega t. \tag{16}$$

Figure 6 shows the instantaneous voltage, current and power waveforms as a function of time. Notice particularly that the instantaneous power p varies with

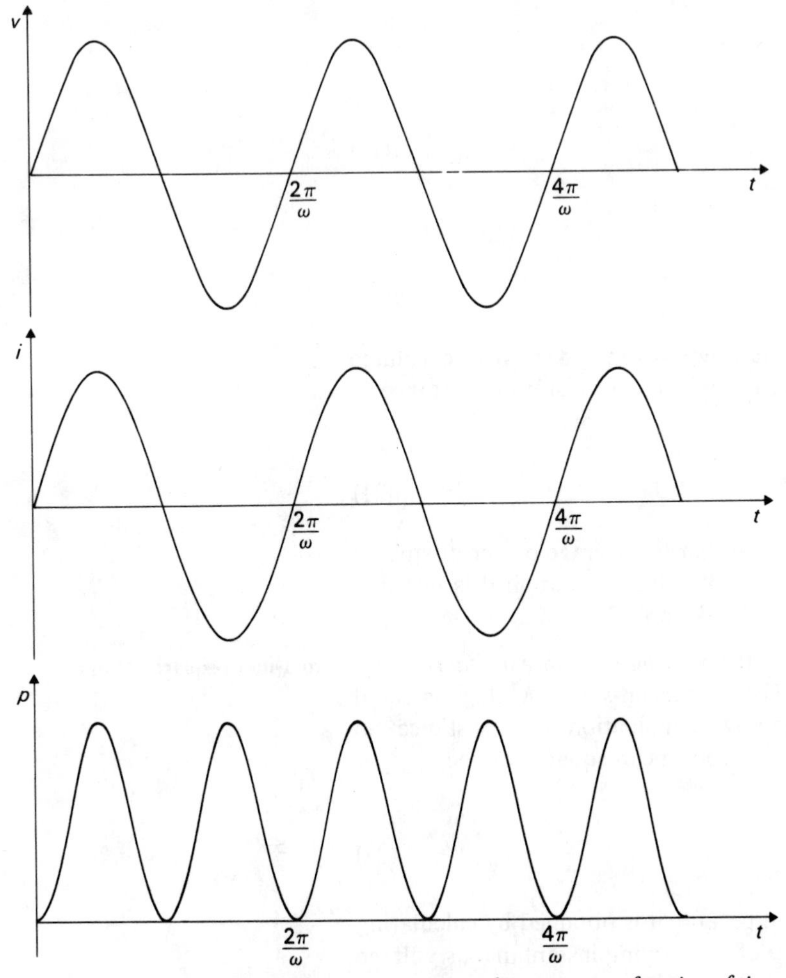

Figure 6 Instantaneous voltage v, current i and power p as a function of time for an alternating voltage applied to a resistor

time, but is always positive because the $\sin^2 \omega t$ term in equation (16) will always be positive. You should also note that voltage and current are *in phase*; that is, the phase difference is zero.

In many applications, instantaneous power is of less practical importance than the *average power* dissipated P. This can be calculated using exactly the same method as that used in section 2.4 to calculate average current. That is

average power

$$P = \frac{\int_0^t p \, dt}{t}. \qquad (17)$$

As before, we take the average over a complete period – from $t = 0$ to $t = 2\pi/\omega$. We can substitute for p from equation (16):

$$P = \frac{\int_0^{2\pi/\omega} (V_m^2/R \sin^2 \omega t) \, dt}{2\pi/\omega}$$

$$= \frac{\omega V_m^2}{2\pi R} \int_0^{2\pi/\omega} \sin^2 \omega t \, dt. \qquad (18)$$

This integral cannot be evaluated directly but we can use the general trigonometric relationship

$$\sin^2 \omega t = \tfrac{1}{2}(1 - \cos 2\omega t).$$

Hence equation (18) becomes

$$P = \frac{\omega V_m^2}{2\pi R} \int_0^{2\pi/\omega} \tfrac{1}{2}(1 - \cos 2\omega t) \, dt$$

$$= \frac{\omega V_m^2}{4\pi R} \int_0^{2\pi/\omega} (1 - \cos 2\omega t) \, dt$$

$$= \frac{\omega V_m^2}{4\pi R} \left[t - \frac{\sin 2\omega t}{2\omega} \right]_0^{2\pi/\omega}$$

$$= \frac{\omega V_m^2}{4\pi R} \left[\frac{2\pi}{\omega} - \frac{\sin 4\pi}{2\omega} - 0 + 0 \right]. \qquad (19)$$

But $\sin 4\pi = 0$, hence equation (19) becomes

$$P = \frac{V_m^2}{2R}. \qquad (20)$$

It is useful to compare this equation with the power dissipated when a d.c. voltage is applied to a resistor. If a d.c. voltage V_m is applied to a resistor of resistance R, the power dissipated $P_{d.c.}$ is

$$P_{d.c.} = \frac{V_m^2}{R}. \qquad (21)$$

So comparing equations (20) and (21) we see that the average power dissipated in a resistance R when an a.c. voltage of peak value V_m is applied is just half the power dissipated when a d.c. voltage V_m is applied.

This result leads directly to the idea of the *root-mean-square voltage* (r.m.s. voltage) when discussing a.c. voltages. The root-mean-square voltage is equal to the d.c. voltage which gives the same power dissipation in a resistance. So for an a.c. voltage with a peak value V_m, the root-mean-square voltage $V_{r.m.s.}$ is given by

root-mean-square voltage

$$V_{r.m.s.} = \frac{V_m}{\sqrt{2}}. \qquad (22)$$

The root-mean-square voltage is so called because it is obtained by calculating the mean, or average, value of the square of the varying instantaneous voltage and taking the square root of the result.

Precisely the same type of argument is used to calculate a *root-mean-square current* (or r.m.s. current). Thus if an alternating current has a peak value of I_m, the r.m.s. current $I_{r.m.s.}$ is given by

root-mean-square current

$$I_{r.m.s.} = \frac{I_m}{\sqrt{2}}. \qquad (23)$$

Root-mean-square values are used almost universally to specify a.c. voltages and currents. The 240 V a.c. mains, for example, has an r.m.s. value of 240 V. Thus the peak voltage of a 240 V mains supply is $240\ \text{V} \times \sqrt{2} = 339\ \text{V}$. Similarly a fuse rated at 13 A means that it will limit current to an r.m.s. value of 13 A. It will pass a peak value of $13\ \text{A} \times \sqrt{2} = 18.4\ \text{A}$.

The advantage of specifying r.m.s. values is that for resistive circuits we may use the equations

$$I_{r.m.s.} = \frac{V_{r.m.s.}}{R} \qquad (24)$$

and

$$P = I_{r.m.s.} \times V_{r.m.s.} \qquad (25)$$

where I, V, R and P refer respectively to current, voltage, resistance and power. So, for example, if a light bulb is rated at 60 W for use on 240 V (r.m.s.) mains, the r.m.s. current drawn when it is in use is, from equation (25), $(60/240)\ \text{A} = 0.25\ \text{A}$ and its resistance under operating conditions is, from equation (24), given by $(240/0.25)\ \Omega = 960\ \Omega$.

SAQ 5 (Objective 4)

(a) What is the r.m.s. value of a sinusoidal voltage of peak value 100 V?

(b) What is the peak value of a sinusoidal voltage of r.m.s. value 100 V?

SAQ 6 (Objectives 2, 3 and 4)

A sinusoidal voltage of r.m.s. value 12 V and frequency 50 Hz is connected to a resistor of resistance 10 Ω.

(a) Write down an equation for the instantaneous applied voltage.

(b) What is the instantaneous current in the resistor?

(c) What is the r.m.s. current in the resistor?

(d) What is the average power P dissipated in the resistor?

3.2 The response of inductors

Consider what happens when a sinusoidal voltage is applied across a lossless inductor such as a coil or wire of zero resistance. Unit 12 showed that instantaneous voltage v and current i are related to the inductance L by the equation

$$v = L\frac{di}{dt}. \qquad (26)$$

Consider a sinusoidal voltage

$$v = V_m \cos \omega t. \qquad (27)$$

(Note we choose the cosine form for voltage because it simplifies the mathematics.) Combining equations (26) and (27) gives

$$V_m \cos \omega t = L\frac{di}{dt}$$

and this can be rearranged to give

$$\frac{di}{dt} = \frac{V_m}{L} \cos \omega t.$$

Such an equation can be integrated by separating the variables:

$$\int di = \frac{V_m}{L} \int \cos \omega t \, dt,$$

which gives

$$i = \frac{V_m}{\omega L} \sin \omega t + \text{constant}. \tag{28}$$

Here then is an equation for the current flowing in the inductor. The constant term represents any constant direct current that may be flowing in the inductor. Such a current does not affect the voltage across a lossless inductor (whose resistance is zero). So we can regard it as zero without affecting our conclusions.

$$i = \frac{V_m}{\omega L} \sin \omega t. \tag{29}$$

Figure 7 shows graphs of v and i as a function of time; that is, it shows graphs of equations (27) and (29). The important feature to note is that current and voltage are not *in-phase*. Current lags behind voltage by a quarter of a cycle; in other words, the instant at which current reaches its maximum value is $\pi/2\omega$ seconds later than the time at which the voltage reaches its peak value.

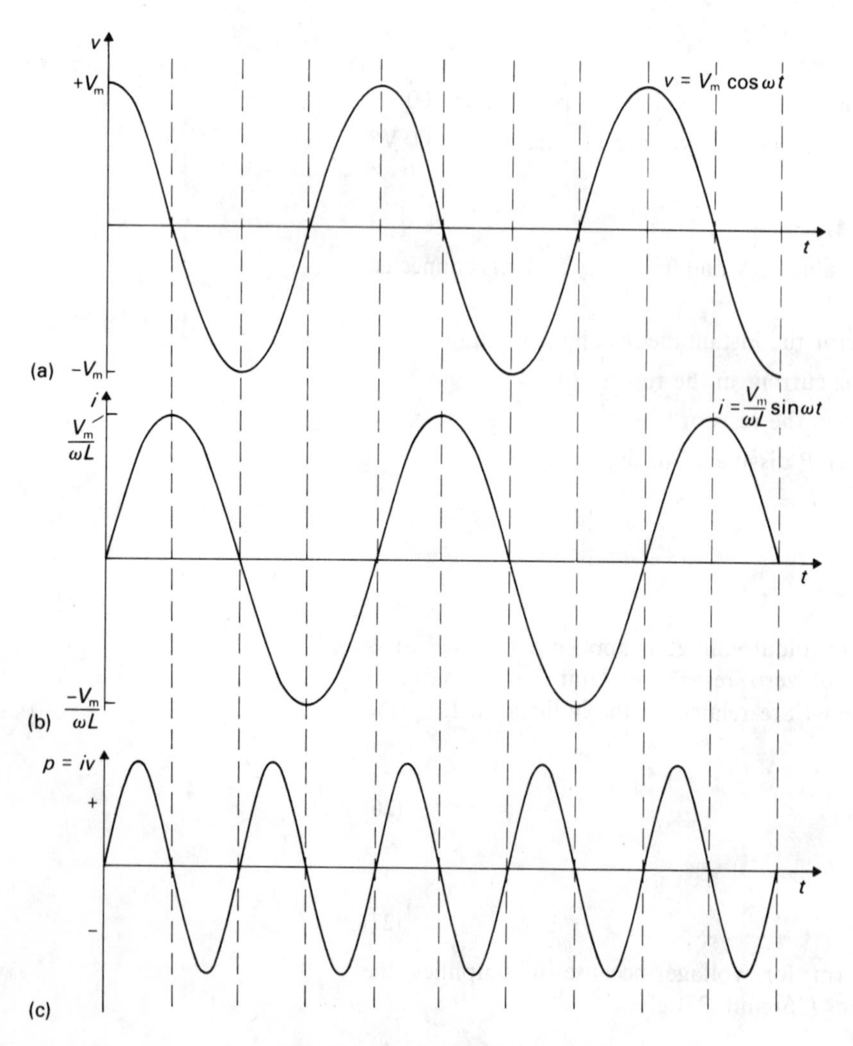

Figure 7 Instantaneous voltage v, current i and power p in a lossless inductor of inductance L. (ω is angular frequency of the applied a.c. voltage)

If we follow our usual practice and write instantaneous current as

$$i = I_m \sin \omega t,$$

then by comparing this with equation (29) you can see that for a lossless inductor, the peak current I_m is given by

$$I_m = \frac{V_m}{\omega L}. \qquad (30)$$

SAQ 7 (Objectives 2, 4, 5)

An a.c. voltage of frequency 50 Hz and peak voltage 12 V is applied across a lossless inductance of 0.5 H. Calculate:

(a) the r.m.s. voltage,

(b) the peak current,

(c) the r.m.s. current,

(d) the equation of the applied instantaneous voltage *as a sine function* if the equation of the instantaneous current is $i = I_m \sin \omega t$.

When current and voltage are not in phase, current flows *against* the voltage for part of each cycle; that is, it flows *up* the potential gradient from the more negative terminal of the inductor *towards* the more positive one. In other parts of the cycle, the reverse is true and current flows down the potential gradient.

You will remember from Unit 10 that when a battery is connected to a resistor, current flows in the external circuit from positive to negative, dissipating power as thermal energy. Inside the battery, current flows from negative to positive, acquiring the electrical energy it then dissipates in the external circuit.

So, when current flows against the potential gradient in an inductor, the inductor is behaving just like the battery and acting as a source of power. Later in the cycle, when current flows down the potential gradient, the inductor acts like an external load attached to a battery and behaves as a sink of power. So when an a.c. voltage is applied to an inductor it alternates between being a source and a sink of power.

This effect can be shown graphically by calculating instantaneous power $p = iv$ for all instants. The resulting graph is shown in Figure 7(c). Note that the power flowing *into* the inductor during parts of the cycle is equal to that flowing *out* at other times because the waveform has equal positive and negative components.

Since the energy flowing into a lossless inductor can be recovered and is not lost, it must be stored in the inductor. In fact it is stored in the magnetic field of the inductor. A device that behaves in this way is called a *reactor*: it can *store* or hold energy and release it again later. It does not dissipate it as heat. It is not, however, a *source* of energy, like a battery. It will only give back energy that it has previously absorbed.

reactor

Lossless inductors are pure reactors. Practical inductors are not quite lossless, so voltage and current are not quite 90° out of phase. As a result, they absorb (and convert to heat) a little more power than they subsequently release again. They are not therefore pure reactors but are still said to be *reactive devices*.

reactive devices

SAQ 8 (Objective 5)

Use equations (27) and (29) to show that the instantaneous power, $p = iv$, varies sinusoidally at twice the frequency of the applied voltage. (You may use the general trigonometric relationship that $\sin 2\theta = 2 \sin \theta \cos \theta$.)

SAQ 9 (Objective 5)

Use the method described in section 3.1 to show that the average power P in a lossless inductor is zero. (You may use the general trigonometric relationship that $\sin 2\theta = 2 \sin \theta \cos \theta$.)

3.3 The response of capacitors

Unit 11 showed that when two conductors were close together with a potential difference V between them, then each conductor would carry a charge Q. These quantities are related to each other by the capacitance C where

$$C = \frac{Q}{V}. \tag{31}$$

So if a varying voltage v is applied to the capacitor, the charge q at any instant varies accordingly. These instantaneous values can be inserted in equation (31) to give

$$C = \frac{q}{v}$$

or

$$q = Cv. \tag{32}$$

Since C is a constant, we may differentiate this equation with respect to time t to give:

$$\frac{dq}{dt} = C\frac{dv}{dt}. \tag{33}$$

But dq/dt, the rate of change of charge with time, is simply instantaneous current i flowing to or from the capacitor. So equation (33) becomes

$$i = C\frac{dv}{dt}. \tag{34}$$

Now suppose that the applied voltage is of the form

$$v = V_m \cos \omega t. \tag{35}$$

So

$$\frac{dv}{dt} = -\omega V_m \sin \omega t,$$

and if this is substituted into equation (34) we get

$$i = -\omega C V_m \sin \omega t. \tag{36}$$

Figure 8 shows plots of v and i as a function of time; that is, graphs of equations (35) and (36). As with an inductor, the instantaneous current and voltage are again *out of phase* by a quarter of a cycle but this time it is the voltage which lags behind the current; in other words, the voltage reaches its maximum value a quarter of a cycle ($\pi/2$ radians) *after* the current has passed through its maximum value.

Again, if we were to write equation (36) in the form

$$i = I_m \sin \omega t, \tag{37}$$

where I_m is the maximum current, then by comparing equations (36) and (37) we see that

$$I_m = -\omega C V_m. \tag{38}$$

SAQ 10 (Objectives 2, 4, 6)

An a.c. voltage of frequency 500 Hz and amplitude 15 V is applied across a capacitance of 0.1 μF. Calculate or write down:

(a) the r.m.s. voltage,

(b) the peak current,

(c) the r.m.s. current,

(d) the equation of the applied instantaneous voltage *as a sine function* if the equation of the instantaneous current is given by $i = I_m \sin \omega t$.

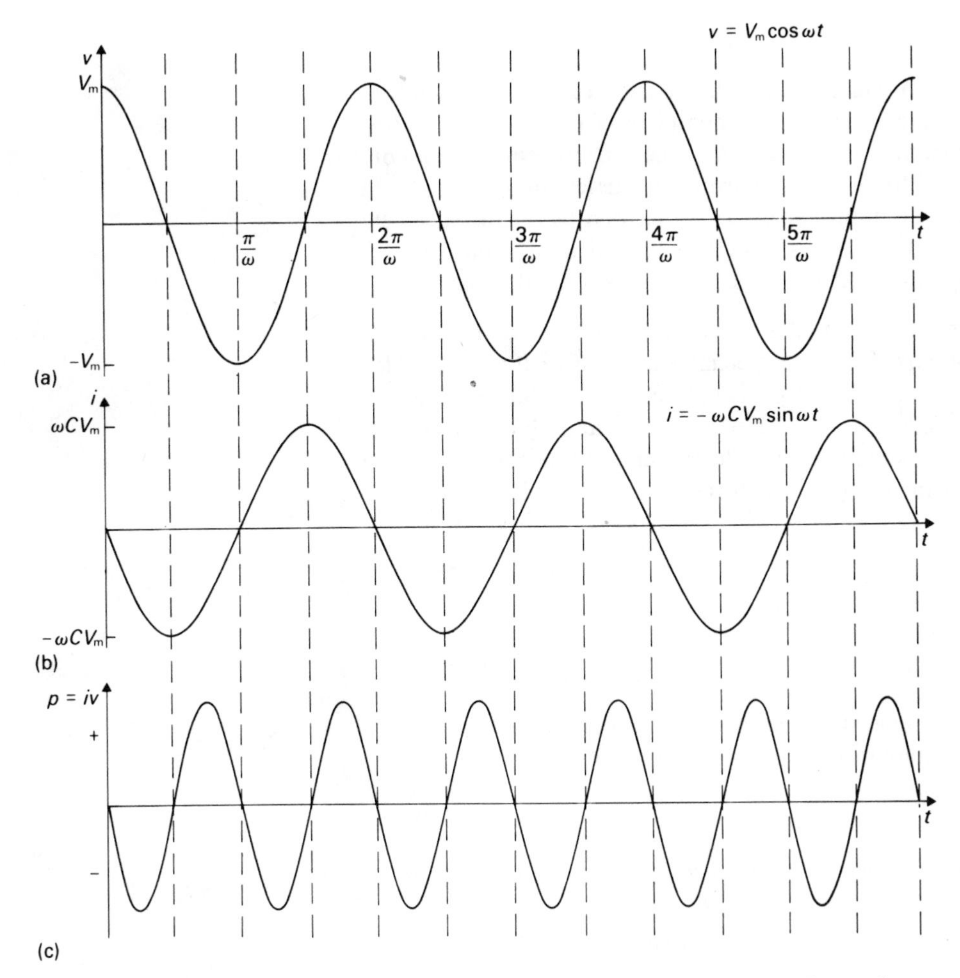

Figure 8 Instantaneous voltage v, current i and power p in a capacitance C (ω is the angular frequency of the applied voltage)

The most striking effect of applying an a.c. voltage to a capacitor is that it conducts current. This is in direct contrast to the response of the capacitor to a d.c. voltage, when it effectively behaves as a break in the circuit and allows no current to flow.

Now the space between the two conductors that form the two plates of a capacitor is an insulator, yet a current seems to flow through it. So if current is thought of *only* as the flow of electrons, it is not possible for current to flow between the plates; a current can only flow in the wires, bringing electrons to one plate and removing them from the other.

displacement current

It turns out, however, that this is not a sufficient description of how current flows. Realising this, James Clerk Maxwell in the 1870s proposed the existence of *displacement current*, which flows across insulating gaps in response to *changes* in potential difference across them. You can think of displacement current in insulators as the *displacement* of electrons towards the positive plate. If the electric field is changing then there will be a small movement of electrons which can be regarded as a current.

However, this is not a true picture for all insulators, since displacement current will flow through a vacuum where there are no electrons! Indeed ε_0, the permittivity of free space, is a measure of how much displacement current flows in response to a changing electric field. Also, since power can flow through empty space by the transmission of electromagnetic waves – such as radio or sunlight – it follows that displacement current is indeed a reality, not just a convenient way of describing the working of capacitors.

The existence of displacement current through capacitors allows us, therefore, to regard circuits containing capacitors as complete circuits for alternating current. The alternating current is present everywhere in the circuit in a continuous loop. For most of the loop the current is carried by electrons, but across the small insulated gap in the capacitor it is carried by the displacement current. No displacement current flows if the *rate of change* of applied potential difference is zero; so, for direct currents, capacitors are still insulators.

Since current and voltage are not in phase with each other, a capacitor acts as a reactive device; that is, for part of the cycle it behaves as a source of power and for the rest of the time it behaves as a sink. By calculating the instantaneous power p as the product $i \times v$, Figure 8(c) is obtained and, as with an inductor, it is clear that there is no net power consumption since the power consumed is equal to the power delivered. In this instance the device stores the energy in the electric field.

3.4 Summary of section 3

1 When an alternating voltage of instantaneous value v is applied to a resistor of resistance R, the instantaneous current i is given by

$$i = \frac{v}{R}.$$

2 When an a.c. voltage is applied to a resistance R, current and voltage are *in phase.*

3 The instantaneous power p dissipated when an a.c. voltage v causes a current i to flow is given by

$$p = iv.$$

4 The average power P dissipated in resistance R when an a.c. voltage of amplitude V_m is applied across it is given by

$$P = \frac{V_m^2}{2R}.$$

5 Root-mean-square voltage $V_{r.m.s.}$ of a sinusoid is related to amplitude V_m by the equation

$$V_{r.m.s.} = \frac{V_m}{\sqrt{2}}.$$

6 Root-mean-square current $I_{r.m.s.}$ of a sinusoid is related to amplitude I_m by the equation

$$I_{r.m.s.} = \frac{I_m}{\sqrt{2}}.$$

7 When an r.m.s. voltage $V_{r.m.s.}$ is applied across a resistance, R, and a current $I_{r.m.s.}$ flows, then

$$I_{r.m.s.} = \frac{V_{r.m.s.}}{R}$$

8 If an instantaneous voltage $v = V_m \cos \omega t$ is applied to a lossless inductance L, the instantaneous current i is given by

$$i = \frac{V_m}{\omega L} \sin \omega t.$$

9 The current in a lossless inductance lags a quarter of a cycle ($\pi/2$ radians) behind the applied voltage.

10 The amplitude I_m of the current flowing in a lossless inductance L is $V_m/\omega L$, where V_m is the amplitude of the applied voltage and ω is the angular frequency of the applied voltage.

11 The average power in a lossless inductor or capacitor is zero.

12 If an instantaneous voltage $v = V_m \cos \omega t$ is applied to a lossless capacitance C, the instantaneous current i is given by

$$i = -\omega C V_m \sin \omega t.$$

13 The current in a lossless capacitor leads the applied voltage by a quarter of a cycle ($\pi/2$ radians).

14 The amplitude I_m of the current flowing in a capacitance C is $\omega C V_m$, where V_m is the amplitude of the applied voltage and ω is the angular frequency of the applied voltage.

You should now be able to attempt questions 526–30 in the *Problem Book*.

---

4 AC CIRCUIT CALCULATIONS

4.1 Resistance and impedance

The resistance of a resistor is the voltage across it divided by the current flowing through it, that is

$$\text{Resistance} = \frac{\text{voltage}}{\text{current}}. \tag{39}$$

This relationship holds true for d.c. voltages and currents, instantaneous a.c. voltages and currents and r.m.s. values. There is therefore no difficulty in defining the resistance of a resistor. However, the reason why this relationship holds true under all circumstances is that the current flowing through the device is always in phase with the applied voltage, so that as voltage changes with time, current changes by the same proportion.

With reactive devices, where current and voltage are not in phase, it is impossible to define a resistance using equation (39). For example consider a circuit containing only a capacitor. If a d.c. voltage is applied, no current will flow and the resistance is infinite. If an a.c. voltage is applied, the current and voltage variations will be as shown in Figures 8(a) and 8(b). At time $t = 0$, v takes a finite positive value but i is zero, so resistance would be positive and infinitely large. At time $t = \pi/2\omega$, v is zero but i now possesses a finite negative value; hence resistance would be zero. When $t = \pi/\omega$, i is zero but v is negative and finite so the resistance would be negative and infinite. By the time $t = 3\pi/2\omega$ the resistance will be zero again. Thus during a single cycle of the applied voltage the resistance would have varied from infinite through zero to infinitely negative and back again.

The parameter corresponding to resistance that is used with reactive devices is called *impedance* (symbol $\boldsymbol{Z}$). Impedance is written in vector notation because it possesses both magnitude and phase. We shall consider the effect of phase shortly, but the magnitude of $\boldsymbol{Z}$ can be applied using r.m.s. values, which do not involve phase. The magnitude of impedance, Z, is defined as

impedance

$$Z = \frac{V_{\text{r.m.s.}}}{I_{\text{r.m.s.}}}. \tag{40}$$

The r.m.s. values of voltage and current of a steady sinusoid do not change with time. Thus, for a circuit containing only a capacitor of capacitance C, section 3.3 showed that if

$$v = V_{\text{m}} \cos \omega t \qquad \text{(from equation 35)}$$

then

$$i = I_{\text{m}} \sin \omega t \qquad \text{(from equation 37)}$$

where

$$I_{\text{m}} = \omega C V_{\text{m}}. \qquad \text{(from equation 38)}$$

Note, we ignore the minus sign in I_{m} because we are considering only the magnitude of the current. But

$$I_{\text{r.m.s.}} = \frac{I_{\text{m}}}{\sqrt{2}} = \frac{\omega C V_{\text{m}}}{\sqrt{2}}$$

and

$$V = \frac{V_{\text{m}}}{\sqrt{2}}.$$

So

$$Z = \frac{V_{\text{r.m.s.}}}{I_{\text{r.m.s.}}} = \frac{1}{\omega C}. \tag{41}$$

So the magnitude of the impedance of the capacitor is $1/\omega C$. Note that the magnitude of the impedance depends on the frequency of the applied a.c. voltage. *For a capacitor*, equation (41) shows that *impedance decreases in magnitude as frequency increases.*

SAQ 11 (Objective 7)

Use equations (27), (30) and (40) to find an expression for the magnitude of the impedance of an inductor.

In SAQ 11 you should have shown that the magnitude of the impedance of the inductor is ωL. Again you will observe that it depends on ω, the angular frequency of the a.c. supply. Unlike capacitors, inductors increase their impedance as the angular frequency increases.

Thus, remembering that Z refers to the *magnitude* of an impedance

$$\text{For a resistor, } Z_R = R. \tag{42}$$

$$\text{For a capacitor, } Z_C = \frac{1}{\omega C}. \tag{43}$$

$$\text{For an inductor, } Z_L = \omega L. \tag{44}$$

The magnitude of impedance is measured in ohms (Ω).

SAQ 12 (Objective 7)

A circuit contains a source of a.c. voltage of amplitude 25 V and frequency 100 Hz connected to a single component. Calculate the r.m.s. current flowing in the circuit if the component is:

(a) a 10 Ω resistor;

(b) a 0.2 H inductor;

(c) a 0.1 μF capacitor.

4.2 Circuits containing more than one component

Look at the circuit in Figure 9. This shows an a.c. voltage connected to a resistor and an inductor in series. Suppose there is a current i flowing in the circuit, where

$$i = I_m \sin \omega t.$$

The potential difference across the resistor is v_R, where

$$v_R = iR$$
$$= I_m R \sin \omega t.$$

The potential difference across the inductor is v_L, where

$$v_L = L\frac{di}{dt}$$
$$= I_m \omega L \cos \omega t.$$

The total voltage across the pair is:

$$v_R + v_L = I_m(R \sin \omega t + \omega L \cos \omega t). \tag{45}$$

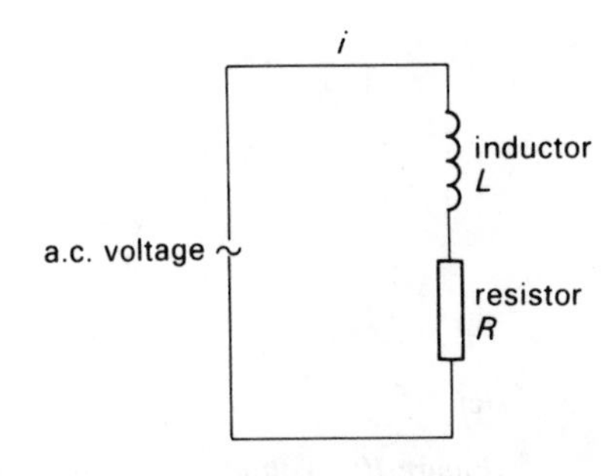

Figure 9 AC circuit containing a resistor and an inductor in series.

Figures 10(a) and 10(b) shows graphs of v_R and v_L as a function of time and Figure 10(c) shows their sum. The sum is again a sinusoid but its r.m.s. value is *not* the sum of the r.m.s. values of v_R and v_L and their combined impedance is not simply the sum of their individual impedances; that is, in this instance,

$$Z_{total} \neq Z_L + Z_R.$$

The reason why these impedances cannot be added directly is that impedances have both magnitude and phase and there are different phase relationships between current and voltage for the different components. So we need a way of stating the impedance of a component which expresses both its magnitude (ωL for inductors, $1/\omega C$ for capacitors and R for resistors) and its voltage–current phase relationship. This is very similar to the problem encountered in Unit 1 when we had to find a way of dealing with quantities that possessed magnitude and direction. In that instance we solved the problem by introducing the idea of a vector. The present problem of combining impedances can be solved in an almost identical manner by drawing a *phasor diagram*.

phasor diagram

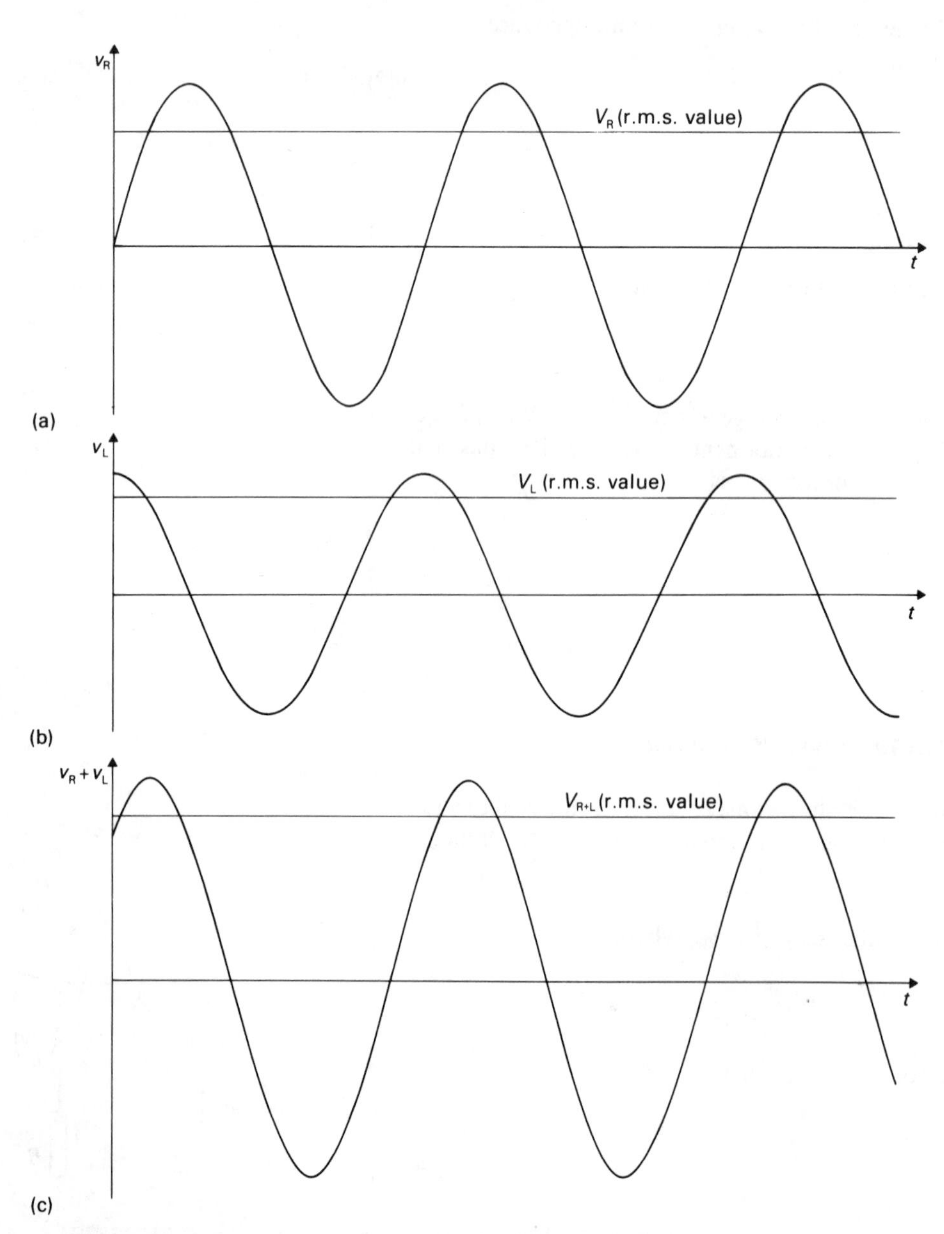

Figure 10 Voltage–time graphs for the circuit of Figure 9. (a) Voltage across the resistor. (b) Voltage across the inductor. (c) The sum of (a) and (b). Note r.m.s. value of curve (c) is not equal to the sum of the r.m.s. values of (a) and (b)

We know that circuit elements in series have the same current flowing through them because currents in a circuit are solenoidal. So it is sensible to take the sinusoidal *current* as the reference phase and to concentrate on how to *add* the corresponding voltages of different relative phases. This means that we need a method of taking account of the fact that in lossless *inductors*, the voltage *leads* the current by 90°, that in lossless capacitors it lags behind the current by 90° and in resistors it is in phase with the current. The clearest way to do this is to adapt the method described in Unit 1 for dealing with vectors. That is, you draw a line, called a *phasor* in this case, whose *length* represents the magnitude of the voltage across a particular circuit element, and whose angle with the x-axis represents the phase angle between the voltage and current. If unit dimension along the x-axis also represents unit current ($i = \sin \omega t$) as reference, then each voltage phasor represents the impedance of the element too.

phasor

So, as in Figure 11, the voltages across three ideal circuit elements are represented by the three phasors along the axes. The diagram adopts the convention that *positive phase angles* are measured anticlockwise from the x-axis as shown, and that a positive value of ϕ corresponds to a *phase lead* of ϕ. So the upward-pointing phasor (ωL) comes earlier, or leads, the resistance phasor by 90°, which in turn leads the downward-pointing phasor ($1/\omega C$) by 90°, as required.

With these conventions clear, it is now a simple matter to add two potential differences in series. They are added in the same way as vectors (representing, say, velocities) are added. You first draw the two phasors representing the two voltages, and then construct a *parallelogram of phasors.* The voltage across the two elements in series is then represented by the phasor that forms the diagonal of the parallelogram.

parallelogram of phasors

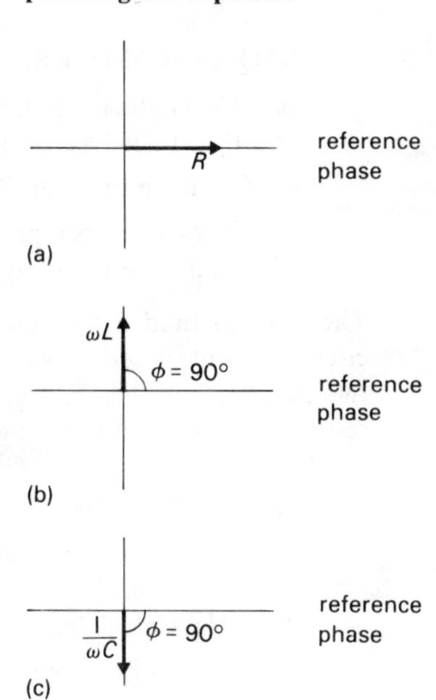

Figure 11 Voltage phasors of circuit elements. (a) Resistor. (b) Inductor. (c) Capacitor.

To show how this is applied, let us return to the two-element circuit of Figure 9, which contains a resistor and an inductor. Using the phasor method outlined above, the phasor diagram will be as shown in Figure 12(a). If the parallelogram (here a rectangle) is constructed as shown in Figure 12(b) then the length of the diagonal, Z, is the magnitude of the combined impedance. Here, because the parallelogram is a rectangle, Z can be calculated using Pythagoras' theorem:

$$Z = \sqrt{(\omega L)^2 + R^2}, \tag{46}$$

and phase angle ϕ is given by

$$\tan \phi = \frac{\omega L}{R}. \tag{47}$$

When a current of 1 A flows in the circuit, the magnitude of the potential difference across *both* elements is Z and this potential is out of phase with the current by a phase angle $+\phi$. In this instance, voltage leads current.

By way of a numerical illustration let us calculate the overall impedance of a lossless inductor of inductance 2 H in series with a resistance of 1 kΩ when the applied a.c. voltage is 50 Hz.

A frequency f can be converted to an angular frequency ω by the equation $\omega = 2\pi f$. Here ω = 50 Hz, so

$$\begin{aligned}\omega &= (2\pi \times 50) \text{ radians s}^{-1}\\ &= 314 \text{ radians s}^{-1}.\end{aligned}$$

So, the magnitude of the impedance of the inductor is

$$\begin{aligned}\omega L &= (314 \times 2)\ \Omega\\ &= 628\ \Omega.\end{aligned}$$

The magnitude of the impedance of the resistor (i.e. its resistance) is 1000 Ω.

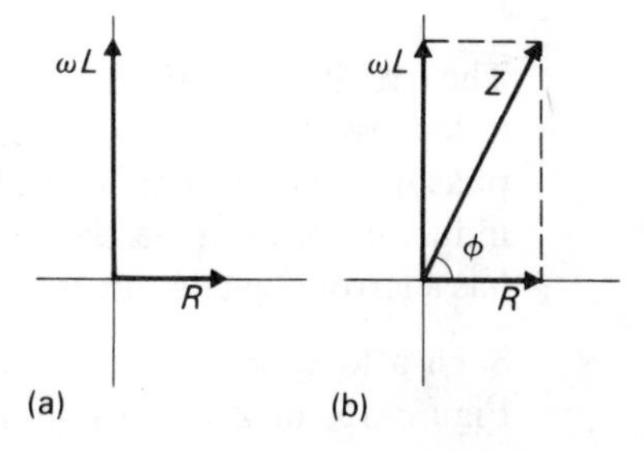

Figure 12 (a) Phasor diagram for the circuit of Figure 9. (b) Parallelograms of phasors to determine the resultant phasor Z

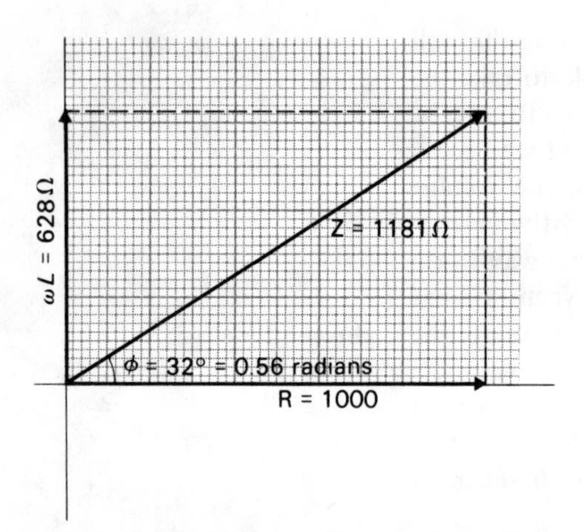

Figure 13 Phasor diagram for an inductor (2 H) *in series with a resistor* (1 kΩ) *at a frequency of* 50 Hz

These may be represented by a phasor diagram as in Figure 13. The overall impedance, including phase angle can be either measured from the diagram directly or (in this instance) calculated using equations (46) and (47). The results are shown in Figure 13.

SAQ 13 (Objective 8)

A lossless inductor of inductance 0.5 H is in series with a resistance of 200 Ω and the applied a.c. voltage has a frequency of 100 Hz.

(a) Calculate the overall impedance of the circuit.

(b) If the current is represented by $i = \sin \omega t$, what equation represents the instantaneous voltage across the two circuit elements?

The same method can be used to analyse circuits containing more than two circuit elements in series, as in Figure 14. The result of combining the phasors for two elements can then be combined with the phasor for the third element. The result is a phasor representing the impedance of all three elements in series.

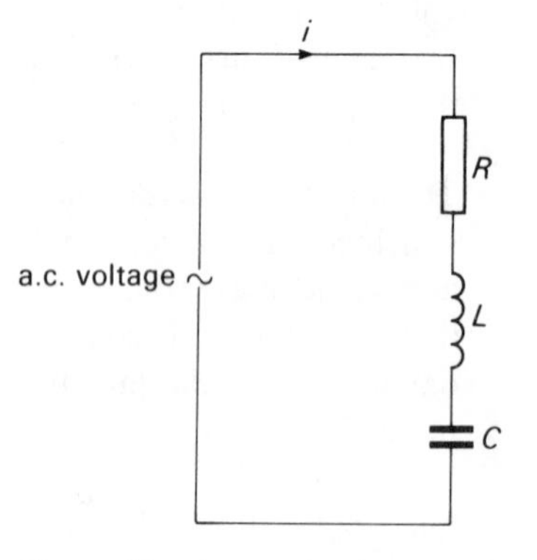

Figure 14 An a.c. circuit containing a resistor, an inductor and a capacitor in series

SAQ 14 (Objective 8)

An a.c. circuit contains an inductance of 0.1 H, a capacitance of 1 μF and a resistance of 0.5 kΩ connected in series. The circuit operates at a frequency of 1 kHz. Calculate:

(a) the magnitude of the impedance of the circuit;

(b) the phase angle between the current in the circuit and the applied voltage.

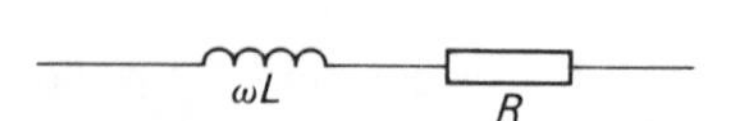

Figure 15 The equivalent circuit of a lossy inductor consists of a lossless inductor of impedance ωL in series with a resistor R

4.3 Ideal and real circuit components

The circuit calculations outlined in section 4.2 treated inductors and capacitors as lossless, and the lines representing their impedances lay along the *y*-axis of the phasor diagram. In practice, however, they are never completely lossless. In an inductor, for example, the windings possess some resistance and if the inductor has a ferromagnetic core it may exhibit hysteresis losses and eddy current losses.

Such a lossy inductor can be represented by the equivalent circuit shown in Figure 15, of a lossless inductance in series with a resistor. The resistance represents all the losses within the inductor; that is, anything that causes heating. The resulting impedance of such a component can be calculated as shown in Figure 16 and, as can be seen, the phasor representing the impedance of this lossy inductor does not lie on the *y*-axis.

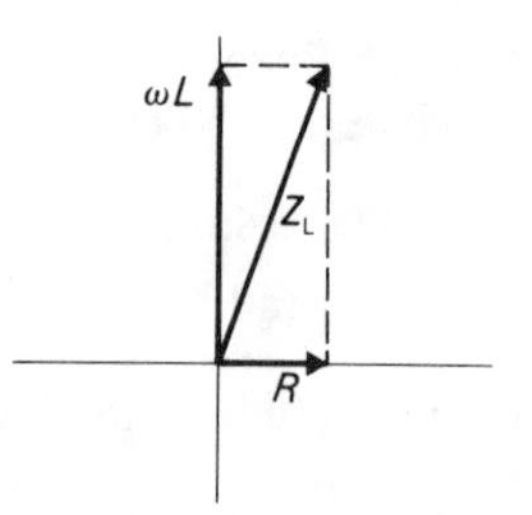

Figure 16 Phasor diagram of the lossy inductor of Figure 15. Note that the impedance Z_L of this inductor does not lie on the y-axis

In capacitors losses occur because the dielectric may not be a perfect insulator, and any conducting materials used in their construction will also possess resistance. It is usual to represent the losses in a capacitor by a parallel resistance, but if the losses are small they can alternatively be represented by a series resistance. So if a capacitor with small losses is represented by a lossless capacitance in series with a resistor, the phasor representing it will not lie on the y-axis but will be in the fourth quadrant of the diagram, as shown in Figure 17.

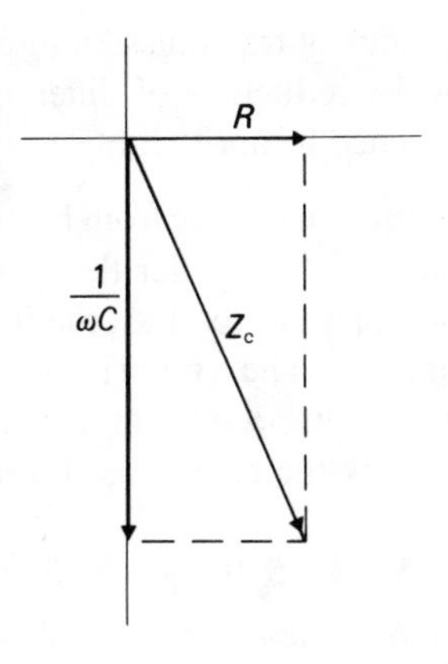

Figure 17 The impedance of a lossy capacitor Z_C can be calculated by representing the capacitor as a lossless capacitor of impedance $1/\omega C$ in series with a resistor R

4.4 Series resonant circuits

When an inductor and a capacitor are in series, as shown in Figure 18(a), their response to a sinusoidal input is quite surprising. Figure 18(b) shows the phasor Z_L representing the impedance of the inductor. It also shows the phasor Z_C representing the impedance of the capacitor. By combining these two phasors using the parallelogram rule the overall impedance Z is obtained.

The striking feature of this calculation is that the magnitude of the resulting impedance Z is *less* than the magnitude of the impedances of either the inductor or the capacitor. So putting two impedances in series when their phase differences approach π radians (180°) can result in a smaller impedance than either component on its own; the whole is less than the sum of the parts.

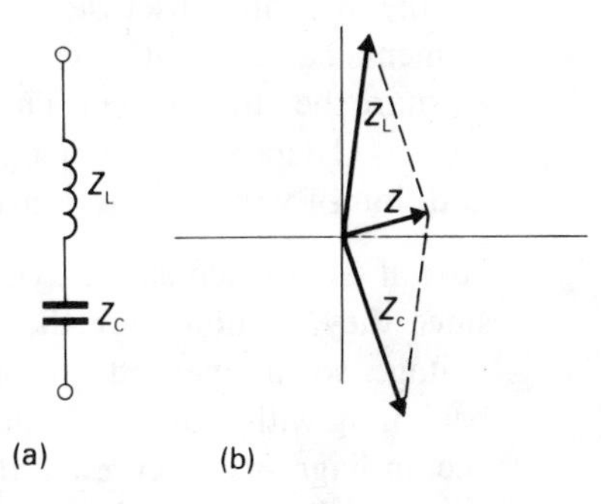

Figure 18 The impedance Z of an inductor and a capacitor in series

Now, of course, the diagram of Figure 18(b) refers to one particular frequency. If the frequency is increased, the impedance of the inductor increases, but the impedance of the capacitor decreases. If the frequency decreases the opposite occurs. Figure 19 (a), (b) and (c) show the phasor diagrams for the same circuit but at different frequencies. If ω is the angular frequency of the middle diagram (it is a repeat of Figure 18b) then Figure 19(a) refers to an angular frequency of $\omega/2$ whilst Figure 19(c) refers to an angular frequency of 2ω. The impedance of the inductor increases with frequency whilst that of the capacitor decreases. The resultant impedance of the two circuit elements in series is larger for both frequencies $\omega/2$ and 2ω. The frequency at which the overall impedance is least is called the *resonance frequency*. So for an applied sinusoidal voltage, the current that flows through the circuit is greatest when the frequency of the sinusoid is equal to the resonance frequency of the circuit.

resonance frequency

It is this property of *resonance* that enables you to tune your radio or television set from one station to another. By adjusting the capacitance of a variable capacitor you can adjust the frequency at which resonance will occur, and so pick out one

resonance

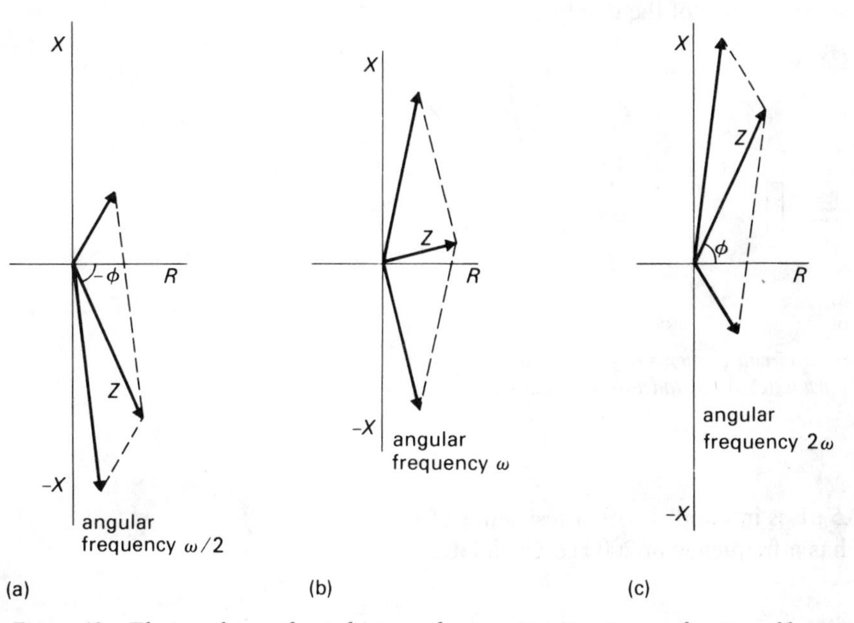

Figure 19 The impedance of an inductor and a capacitor in series as a function of frequency

frequency of transmission in preference to all the others. Similarly, by switching between inductors of different inductances you can select one wave-band in preference to another.

Perhaps you can see from Figure 19 that the smaller the losses in the inductor and capacitor, the smaller the overall resistance at resonance. If both inductor and capacitor were lossless, the impedance of the resonant circuit would be zero at resonance. The smaller the losses in the reactive elements, the smaller the minimum impedance at resonance and the more selective of a particular resonant frequency the circuit becomes.

SAQ 15 (Objective 8)

A lossless capacitor of capacitance C is in series with a lossless inductor of inductance L. If the resonance frequency of the combination is ω, calculate ω in terms of L and C.

4.5 Impedances in parallel

All the foregoing discussion concerning the response of combinations of circuit elements has concentrated on *series* combinations, so the components involved all share the same current. The method of constructing phasor diagrams that has been used depends on this fact, since the diagrams were concerned with the vector addition of voltages, given a unit reference sinusoidal current.

Now if circuit elements are connected in *parallel*, the method cannot be applied since they do not share the same current. They do however share the same voltage, so the method can be adapted to deal with parallel arrangements by beginning with a unit sinusoidal *voltage* as the common reference and drawing vector diagrams to represent the currents through the circuit elements, of lengths equal to the *reciprocals* of their impedances.

Thus, with unit *current*, we saw that the corresponding voltages represent element impedances of magnitude ωL, $1/\omega C$ and R. Now with unit voltages as the reference, the corresponding currents represent the reciprocals of these impedances, namely $1/\omega L$, ωC and $1/R$. Such quantities are called *admittances*. The phases are similarly inverted; that is, in a capacitance, since the voltage lags behind the current, the current *leads* the voltage. So the phasor representing the admittance of a capacitor is drawn 'upwards' in the diagram as indicated in Figure 20(a). A parallel combination of a capacitor and a resistor is represented as in Figure 20(b). The length of the diagonal of the parallelogram constructed from the two admittances represents the admittance of the combination.

admittance

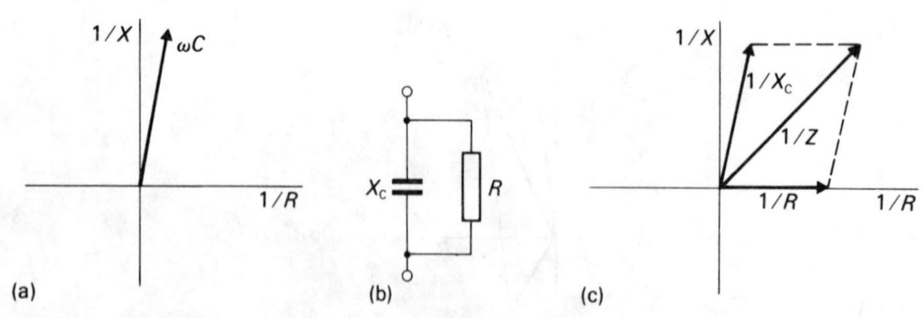

Figure 20 Admittance phasor diagrams for circuit elements in parallel. (a) The admittance of a lossy capacitor. (b) The circuit diagram. (c) Admittance of capacitor and resistor in parallel.

SAQ 16 (Objective 9)

A capacitor of capacitance 0.5 μF is in parallel with a resistance of 10 kΩ and the applied a.c. voltage has a frequency of 200 Hz. Calculate:

(a) the overall admittance,

(b) the overall impedance,

(c) the instantaneous current through the circuit if the applied reference voltage is of the form $v = \sin \omega t$.

SAQ 17 (Objective 9)

(a) Suppose we represent the losses of an inductance and a capacitance by *parallel* resistances. In which quadrant of an admittance phasor diagram will the phasors for (i) the current through the lossy inductor and (ii) the current through the lossy capacitor lie? The reference phasor here is a unit sinusoidal voltage.

(b) What *impedance* would you expect a resonant circuit, consisting of an inductor and a capacitor in parallel, to possess, as compared with the magnitude of the impedance of each element on its own?

Most actual circuits comprise elements interconnected in arrangements that are partly parallel and partly series. These can usually be dealt with by dividing up the circuit into a *series* of smaller *parallel* arrangements. The equivalent impedance of each small parallel arrangement can then be regarded as one of a set of impedances in series. More commonly, however, such circuits are dealt with using an algebraic method, derived from the phasor diagram, but this is a topic left to later courses.

4.6 Transformer calculations

Unit 12 showed that the input current to a transformer with a resistive load (Figure 21a) consisted of two parts: a magnetising current of amplitude I_m and an extra current of amplitude I_e needed to balance the output current into the load resistor.

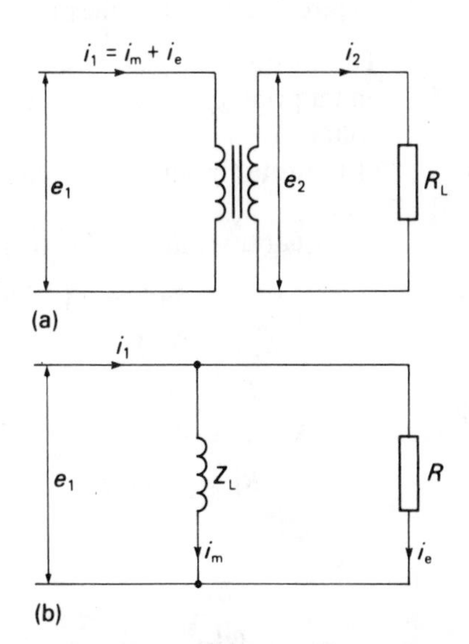

Figure 21 (a) Circuit with resistive load R_L on the secondary. (b) Equivalent circuit of the primary of the transformer in (a)

We are now in a position to calculate the total input current when the applied voltage is sinusoidal. The two instantaneous currents i_m and i_e can be considered as flowing in two parallel impedances, one inductive and the other resistive if the secondary load is resistive. See Figure 21(a).

If L_1 is the inductance of the primary winding, $e_1 = L_1\, di_m/dt$. So if

$$i_m = I_m \sin \omega t,$$

then

$$e_1 = L_1 \omega I_m \cos \omega t.$$

The amplitude of this applied voltage, E_1, is thus

$$E_1 = L_1 \omega I_m,$$

so

$$I_m = \frac{E_1}{L_1 \omega}$$

and the phase of I_m lags 90° behind the voltage E_1. The magnitude of the admittance of the primary winding is therefore $1/L_1\omega$.

Finding Z_R, the impedance of R, is not so straightforward because R represents the load resistance in the secondary, R_L, as 'seen' by the primary circuit. Section 6.2.5. of Unit 12 gives the results

$$i_2 N_2 = i_e N_1 \qquad (48)$$

and

$$\frac{e_1}{e_2} = \frac{N_1}{N_2}. \qquad (49)$$

From (48)

$$i_e = \frac{i_2 N_2}{N_1}.$$

But we know that $i_2 = e_2/R_L$, where R_L is the load resistance in the secondary circuit. So

$$i_e = \frac{e_2}{R_L}\frac{N_2}{N_1}.$$

From (49), $e_2 = e_1 N_2/N_1$, and e_1 and e_2 are always in phase. So

$$i_e = \frac{e_1}{R_L}\left(\frac{N_2}{N_1}\right)^2.$$

The current i_e is always in phase with e_1, so we can rewrite this in terms of amplitude. Thus

$$I_e = \frac{E}{R_L}\left(\frac{N_2}{N_1}\right)^2.$$

So R, the resistance of R_L as seen by the primary, is $R_L(N_1/N_2)^2$. Alternatively R can be regarded as an admittance of

$$\frac{1}{R_L}\left(\frac{N_2}{N_1}\right)^2.$$

Figure 22 is therefore the phasor diagram for the two admittances in Figure 21(b).

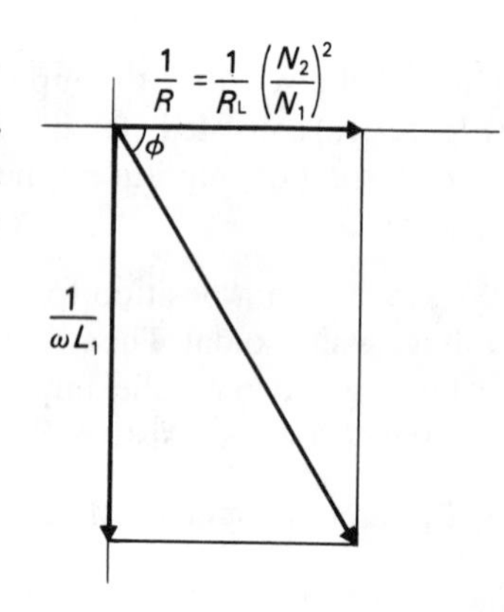

Figure 22 Phasor diagram of Figure 21

To illustrate this, let us suppose a transformer has a turns ratio $N_1:N_2 = 1:4$ and a primary inductance of 0.5 H. If the load resistance is 1 kΩ and the input voltage is of amplitude 10 V and frequency 50 Hz, what are (a) the amplitude of the total input current and (b) its phase relative to the input voltage?

The quantities needed for this calculation are:

$$\omega = 2\pi f = 314 \text{ radians per second,}$$
$$L = 0.5\text{ H}$$
$$E_1 = 10\text{ V}$$
$$N_2/N_1 = 4$$
$$R_L = 1000\ \Omega$$

So

$$I_m = \frac{E_1}{\omega L_1} = \frac{10}{314 \times 0.5}\text{ A} = 0.0637\text{ A}$$

and

$$I_e = \frac{E_1}{R_L}\left(\frac{N_2}{N_1}\right)^2 = \left(\frac{10}{1000} \times 16\right)\text{A} = 0.16\text{ A.}$$

So the amplitude of the total input current is

$$I_{total} = \sqrt{(I_m^2 + I_e^2)} = 0.17\text{ A.}$$

The phase of I_{total} relative to the input voltage is given by

$$\tan\phi = \frac{1}{\omega L_1} \times R_L\left(\frac{N_1}{N_2}\right)^2$$

$$= \frac{I_m}{E_1} \times \frac{E_1}{I_e}$$

$$= \frac{I_m}{I_e}$$

$$= \frac{0.0637}{0.16}$$

$$= 0.398.$$

So $\phi = 21.7°$. The current lags 21.7° behind the voltage.

4.7 Summary of section 4

1 For a single component in a circuit, the magnitude of the impedance Z is given by

$$Z = \frac{V_{\text{r.m.s.}}}{I_{\text{r.m.s.}}},$$

where $V_{\text{r.m.s.}}$ and $I_{\text{r.m.s.}}$ are the r.m.s. values of voltage and current.

2 The magnitudes of the impedances of resistors, inductors and capacitors are

$$Z_R = R,$$

$$Z_L = \omega L,$$

$$Z_C = \frac{1}{\omega C},$$

where R is resistance, L is inductance, C is capacitance, and ω is angular frequency of the applied voltage.

3 When a circuit contains two or more components *in series*, the overall impedance can be calculated using an impedance phasor diagram in which the reference phase is that of the common current. This will also give the phase angle between the overall voltage and the current flowing.

4 When a circuit contains two or more components *in parallel*, the overall impedance can be calculated using an admittance phasor diagram in which the reference phase is that of the common applied voltage. This will also give the phase angle between the current and voltage.

5 When a circuit contains two components in series with relative phase angles approaching 180° (π radians), the overall impedance can reach very low values at the resonance frequency, when the magnitudes of the impedances are almost equal.

You should now be able to attempt questions 531–5 in the *Problem Book.*

---

5 POWER DISSIPATION

5.1 Power dissipated in lossy reactive elements

We have seen that the average power dissipated in a resistor of resistance R when a sinusoidal voltage is applied is $V_m^2/2R$, where V_m is the amplitude of the applied voltage. We have also seen that no average power is dissipated in a lossless reactor. Energy flows into and out of the reactive device twice for each cycle of the applied waveform. We would expect, therefore, that a *lossy* reactive device would dissipate power at a lesser, but finite rate, as compared with the dissipation in a resistor.

If the applied instantaneous voltage to a lossy reactive device is given by

$$v = V_m \sin \omega t$$

then the current in the device will be of the form

$$i = I_m \sin(\omega t + \phi),$$

where ϕ is the phase difference between current and voltage. As you know from earlier in this unit, ϕ may lie between $+\pi/2$ or $-\pi/2$ radians depending on the type of component but it is seldom as large as these limits in practice.

The instantaneous power dissipated p is therefore given by

$$\begin{aligned} p &= vi \\ &= (V_m I_m \sin \omega t) \times \sin(\omega t + \phi). \end{aligned} \qquad (50)$$

The average power dissipation P can be calculated as earlier by integrating this equation over one cycle and dividing by the period of one cycle. That is

$$P = \frac{V_m I_m \int_0^{2\pi/\omega} (\sin \omega t) \sin(\omega t + \phi)\, dt}{2\pi/\omega} \qquad (51)$$

The integration involves simplifying the trigonometric functions to an integrable form and you are not expected to be able to do this. When evaluated, equation (51) gives:

$$P = \frac{V_m I_m}{2} \cos \phi \qquad (52)$$

This is the same as for a resistor except for the factor $\cos \phi$. This factor shows that P decreases as ϕ changes from zero to $\pi/2$ or from zero to $-\pi/2$, since $\cos \phi$ decreases from 1 to zero over either of these ranges.

The factor $\cos \phi$ in equation (52) is called the *power factor*. With a resistive load, current and voltage are in phase, so $\phi = 0$ and $\cos \phi = 1$. Hence power dissipated is $V_m I_m/2$ as expected. With a wholly reactive load, $\phi = \pi/2$ for an inductor or $\phi = -\pi/2$ for a capacitor. In both cases $\cos \phi = 0$ and so the average power dissipated is zero.

5.2 The importance of power factor

Suppose an electric motor is delivering, say, 1 horsepower, or about 750 watts. At least this much power must be drawn from the electricity supply. If the power factor is 1 then on a 250 V a.c. supply the current needed would be at least 3 A; (i.e. 250 V × 3 A = 750 W). Friction and other losses in the motor mean that a little more would actually be needed. But suppose the power factor is 0.5. That is, the phase difference between current and voltage is 60° (i.e. cos 60° = 0.5). The reason why the power factor may be less than 1 is simply that an electric motor might present the source with a mainly inductive impedance, causing the voltage and current to be out of phase. The relationship is now

$$VI \cos \phi = 750 \text{ W}$$

so

$$I = \left(\frac{750}{0.5 \times 250}\right) \text{A}$$

$$= 6 \text{ A}.$$

So, with a power factor of 0.5, twice as much current must be drawn from the sinusoidal source to obtain the same amount of work from the electric motor!

The extra current is undesirable because copper losses in generator windings or transformers or in power transmission cables are proportional to the *square* of the current. So supplying more current than is really needed to give the required power output simply causes unnecessary heat generation, and might even cause damage. So the maximum ratings of an a.c. supply are stated in volt–amps, rather than watts. Just stating the maximum power that can be supplied does not limit the current that may be drawn. Currents through a generator can cause overheating in it even when it is supplying zero power to a reactive load.

Of course, electric motors are always somewhat inductive since the windings on the stator or the rotor are essentially inductors. But, as in transformers, the current that does the work, as distinct from the magnetising current, is in phase with the supply voltage, so the net current lags by less than 90°.

power factor correction

Power factor correction can be applied to an inductive load, such as a motor, by connecting a capacitor across its terminals as in Figure 23. This ensures that the net current drawn by the motor and capacitor is more nearly in phase with the supply voltage. It may seem odd that placing an extra circuit element in parallel with the load, so that an extra current is drawn from the supply, results in *less* net current being supplied; but that is what happens. The lag of one current is balanced by the lead of the other. The reactive current in the motor flows in the capacitor and does no work; so the generator only has to supply the useful current.

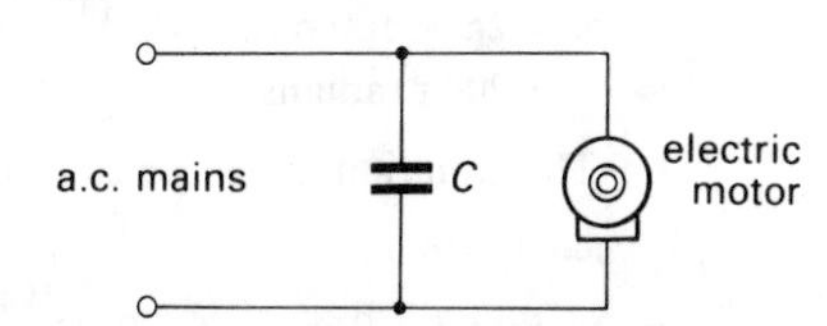

Figure 23 Connecting a capacitor across an electric motor increases the power factor of the motor

SAQ 18 (Objective 10)

A particular inductive motor can be represented by an inductance of 2 H in parallel with a resistance of 500 Ω. At the mains frequency of 50 Hz, what power factor will the load possess?

5.3 Summary of section 5

1 The average power P dissipated in an a.c. circuit is given by

$$P = \tfrac{1}{2}V_m I_m \cos \phi,$$

where V_m and I_m are the peak values of voltage and current and ϕ is the phase difference between current and voltage.

2 Cos ϕ is called the power factor.

3 Power factor must be kept close to a value of 1 in practical machines; power factor correction of an inductive load can be achieved by placing a suitable capacitor across the load.

You should now be able to attempt questions 536–40 in the *Problem Book*.

ANSWERS TO SELF-ASSESSMENT QUESTIONS

SAQ 1

Using the data given in the question,

$$V_m = 5 \text{ V},$$
$$f = 1000 \text{ Hz}.$$

So from equation (2)

$$\omega = 2\pi f$$
$$= (2\pi \times 1000) \text{ radians per second}$$
$$= 2000\pi \text{ radians per second}.$$

So equation is

$$v = 5 \sin 2000\pi t \text{ volts}.$$

Note it is usual to leave the symbol π in the expression rather than write 6283 for 2000π because it often simplifies the plotting of graphs such as that shown in Figure 3. However, if you did evaluate it to give $v = 5 \sin 6283t$ your answer is correct.

SAQ 2

(a) Time for one cycle is $1/f$, where f is frequency (100 Hz in this case). So time for one cycle is

$$\frac{1}{100} \text{ s} = 0.01 \text{ s}.$$

(b) From equation (2) $\omega = 2\pi f$, so

$$\omega = 2\pi \times 100 \text{ radians s}^{-1}$$
$$= 200\pi \text{ radians s}^{-1}.$$

(c) The equation of the sinusoid is of the form

$$i = I_m \sin \omega t,$$

given that $i = 0$ when $t = 0$. Here $I_m = 2$ A and $\omega = 200\pi$ (from (b) above), so

$$i = 2 \sin 200\omega t$$
$$= 2 \sin 628t.$$

SAQ 3

This is a direct application of equation (10). Here

$$t_d = 5 \times 10^{-3} \text{ s}$$

and

$$\omega = 1000 \text{ s}^{-1}.$$

So

$$\phi = \omega t_d$$
$$= 1000 \times 5 \times 10^{-3} \text{ radians}$$
$$= 5 \text{ radians}.$$

SAQ 4

Let the output instantaneous voltage from winding 1 be v_1 where

$$v_1 = V_m \sin \omega t.$$

Here $V_m = 350$ V and frequency $f = 50$ Hz. Thus

$$\omega = 2\pi f$$
$$= (2\pi \times 50) \text{ radians per second}$$
$$= 100\pi \text{ radians per second}$$

So the equation for v_1 will be

$$v_1 = 350 \sin 100\pi t \text{ volts}.$$

The windings are uniformly spaced around the stator, so they will be 120° apart. Now,

$$120° = \frac{120}{360} \times 2\pi \text{ radians}$$
$$= \frac{2\pi}{3} \text{ radians}.$$

So the instantaneous voltage from the second winding, v_2, will lag behind v_1 by an amount $2\pi/3$ radians. In other words, the phase difference is $2\pi/3$ radians. Hence the equation for v_2 will be

$$v_2 = 350 \sin(100\pi t - 2\pi/3) \text{ volts}.$$

By a similar argument, the instantaneous voltage from winding number 3 will lag behind v_1 by a phase angle of $4\pi/3$. So the equation of v_3 is

$$v_3 = 350 \sin(100\pi t - 4\pi/3) \text{ volts}.$$

Alternatively, you could say that v_3 *leads* v_1 by $2\pi/3$ radians. In that case the equation would be

$$v_3 = 350 \sin(100\pi t + 2\pi/3) \text{ volts}.$$

SAQ 5

(a) $$V_{\text{r.m.s.}} = \frac{V_m}{\sqrt{2}}$$
$$= \frac{100}{\sqrt{2}} \text{ V}$$
$$= 70.7 \text{ V}.$$

(b) $$V_m = \sqrt{2} \times V_{\text{r.m.s.}}$$
$$= \sqrt{2} \times 100 \text{ V}$$
$$= 141.4 \text{ V}.$$

SAQ 6

(a) The instantaneous applied voltage v will be of the form $v = V_m \sin \omega t$. We are given $V_{\text{r.m.s.}} = 12$ V. Now,

$$V_m = \sqrt{2} V_{\text{r.m.s.}}$$
$$= (\sqrt{2} \times 12) \text{ V}$$
$$= 17 \text{ V (almost)}.$$

Frequency $f = 50$ Hz, and $\omega = 2\pi f$, so

$$\omega = 100\pi \text{ radians s}^{-1}.$$

Hence the equation of the applied voltage is

$$v = 17 \sin 100\pi t \text{ volts}.$$

(b) The instantaneous current i is given by

$$i = \frac{v}{R},$$

where R is the circuit resistance. Now, $v = 17 \sin 100\pi t$ volts and R is 10 Ω, so

$$i = 1.7 \sin 100\pi t \text{ amperes}.$$

(c) $$I_{\text{r.m.s.}} = \frac{V_{\text{r.m.s.}}}{R}.$$

We are given that $V_{\text{r.m.s.}} = 12$ V and $R = 10$ Ω, so

$$I_{\text{r.m.s.}} = \frac{12}{10} \text{ A}$$
$$= 1.2 \text{ A}.$$

(d) $P = I_{\text{r.m.s.}} \times V_{\text{r.m.s.}}$

$I_{\text{r.m.s.}} = 1.2\ \text{A}$ (calculated above)

$V_{\text{r.m.s.}} = 12\ \text{V}$ (given).

So

$$P = (1.2 \times 12)\ \text{W} = 14.4\ \text{W}.$$

SAQ 7

(a) $$V_{\text{r.m.s.}} = \frac{V_m}{\sqrt{2}} = \frac{12}{\sqrt{2}}\ \text{V} = 8.5\ \text{V}.$$

(b) Peak current I_m is given by

$$I_m = \omega \frac{V_m}{L}$$

Here $V_m = 12$ V, $L = 0.5$ H and

$$\omega = 2\pi f = 100\pi\ \text{radians s}^{-1}.$$

So

$$I_m = \frac{12}{0.5 \times 100\pi}\ \text{A} = 0.076\ \text{A} = 76\ \text{mA}.$$

(c) $$I_{\text{r.m.s.}} = \frac{I_m}{\sqrt{2}} = \frac{76}{\sqrt{2}}\ \text{mA} = 54\ \text{mA}.$$

(d) If $i = I_m \sin \omega t$ then $v = V_m \sin(\omega t + \phi)$. But we know that voltage *leads* current by a quarter of a cycle; that is, the phase angle ϕ must be $\pi/2$ so

$$v = V_m \sin\left(\omega t + \frac{\pi}{2}\right).$$

SAQ 8

The equations for instantaneous voltage and current are:

$$v = V_m \cos \omega t$$

$$i = \frac{V_m}{\omega L} \sin \omega t.$$

So instantaneous power p is given by

$$p = iv = (V_m \cos \omega t) \times \frac{V_m}{\omega L} \sin \omega t = \frac{V_m^2}{\omega L} \cos \omega t \sin \omega t.$$

But $2 \sin \omega t \cos \omega t = \sin 2\omega t$, so

$$p = \frac{V_m^2}{2\omega L} \sin 2\omega t.$$

This is the equation of a sinusoidal waveform of angular frequency 2ω; i.e. twice the frequency of the applied voltage.

SAQ 9

Average power P is given by:

$$P = \frac{\int_0^t p\, dt}{t} = \frac{\int_0^t iv\, dt}{t}.$$

Average over a complete cycle is:

$$P = \frac{\int_0^{2\pi/\omega} (V_m \cos \omega t)(V_m/\omega L) \sin \omega t\, dt}{2\pi/\omega}$$

$$= \frac{V_m^2}{2\pi L} \int_0^{2\pi/\omega} \cos \omega t \sin \omega t\, dt$$

$$= \frac{V_m^2}{4\pi L} \int_0^{2\pi/\omega} \sin 2\omega t\, dt$$

$$= \frac{V_m^2}{4\pi L} \left[-\frac{\cos 2\omega t}{2\omega} \right]_0^{2\pi/\omega}$$

$$= \frac{V_m^2}{8\pi\omega L} (-\cos 4\pi + \cos 0)$$

$$= \frac{V_m^2}{8\pi\omega L} (-1 + 1)$$

$$= 0.$$

Average power is zero.

SAQ 10

(a) $$V_{\text{r.m.s.}} = \frac{V_m}{\sqrt{2}} = \frac{15}{\sqrt{2}}\ \text{V} = 10.6\ \text{V}.$$

(b) $I_m = \omega C V_m$, as given by equation (38). Note that the minus sign in equation (38) may be ignored when calculating the magnitude of the current. Here

$$C = 0.1\ \mu\text{F} = 0.1 \times 10^{-6}\ \text{F},$$

$$V_m = 15\ \text{V}$$

and

$$\omega = 2\pi f = 10^3\pi\ \text{radians per second.}$$

So

$$I_m = (0.1 \times 10^{-6} \times 15 \times 10^3\pi)\ \text{A} = 0.0047\ \text{A} = 4.7\ \text{mA}.$$

(c) $$I_{\text{r.m.s.}} = \frac{I_m}{\sqrt{2}} = \frac{4.7}{\sqrt{2}}\ \text{mA} = 3.3\ \text{mA}.$$

(d) If $i = I_m \sin \omega t$ then $v = V_m \sin(\omega t + \phi)$. But voltage *lags* behind current by a quarter cycle ($\pi/2$ radians), so $\phi = -\pi/2$. Thus

$$v = V_m \sin(\omega t - \pi/2).$$

SAQ 11

From equation (27): $v = V_m \cos \omega t$.

From equation (30): $I_m = \dfrac{V_m}{\omega L}$.

From equation (40): $Z = \dfrac{V_{r.m.s.}}{I_{r.m.s.}}$.

But

$$V_{r.m.s.} = \frac{V_m}{\sqrt{2}}$$

and

$$I_{r.m.s.} = \frac{I_m}{\sqrt{2}} = \frac{V_m}{\omega L\sqrt{2}}$$

so

$$Z = \frac{V_{r.m.s.}}{I_{r.m.s.}} = \frac{V_m/\sqrt{2}}{V_m/\omega L\sqrt{2}}.$$

So

$$Z = \omega L.$$

SAQ 12

The peak voltage V_m is 25 V, so

$$V_{r.m.s.} = \frac{V_m}{\sqrt{2}} = 17.7 \text{ V}.$$

The angular frequency is

$$\omega = 2\pi f = 2\pi \times 100 \text{ radians s}^{-1} = 200\pi \text{ radians s}^{-1} = 628 \text{ radians s}^{-1}.$$

(a) For a 10 Ω resistor,

$$Z_R = R = 10\ \Omega.$$

Now

$$Z_R = \frac{V_{r.m.s.}}{I_{r.m.s.}},$$

so

$$I_{r.m.s.} = \frac{V_{r.m.s.}}{Z_R} = \frac{17.7}{10} \text{ A} = 1.77 \text{ A}.$$

(b) For a 0.2 H inductor,

$$Z_L = \omega L = (628 \times 0.2)\ \Omega = 125.6\ \Omega.$$

So

$$I_{r.m.s.} = \frac{V_{r.m.s.}}{Z_L} = \frac{17.7}{125.6} \text{ A} = 0.14 \text{ A}.$$

(c) For a 0.1 μF capacitor,

$$Z_C = \frac{1}{\omega C} = \frac{1}{628 \times 0.1 \times 10^{-6}}\ \Omega = 1.59 \times 10^4\ \Omega.$$

$$I_{r.m.s.} = \frac{V_{r.m.s.}}{Z_C} = \frac{17.7}{1.59 \times 10^4} \text{ A} = 0.0011 \text{ A} = 1.1 \text{ mA}.$$

SAQ 13

This question is similar to the worked example in the text.

Angular frequency $\omega = 2\pi f = (2\pi \times 100) \text{ radians s}^{-1} = 628 \text{ radians s}^{-1}$.

Impedance of inductor $\omega L = (628 \times 0.5)\ \Omega = 314\ \Omega$.

Impedance of resistor $R = 200\ \Omega$.

(a) The overall impedance is given by Z where

$$Z = \sqrt{314^2 + 200^2}\ \Omega = 372\ \Omega.$$

(b) If phase angle is ϕ,

$$\tan \phi = \frac{\omega L}{R} = \frac{314}{200},$$

so

$$\phi = 57.5^\circ = 1 \text{ radian}$$

So if $i = \sin \omega t$, then

$$v = 372 \sin(\omega t + 1) \text{ volts}.$$

SAQ 14

Angular frequency $\omega = 2\pi f = (2\pi \times 1000) \text{ radians s}^{-1} = 6283 \text{ radians s}^{-1}$.

Impedance of inductor $\omega L = (6283 \times 0.1)\ \Omega = 628\ \Omega$.

Impedance of capacitor $1/\omega C = (1/6283 \times 10^{-6})\ \Omega = 159\ \Omega$.

Impedance of resistor $R = 500\ \Omega$.

(a) The phasor diagram for this circuit is shown in Figure 24. By constructing the parallelogram OABC the resultant Z' of R and ωL can be obtained graphically or by calculation. If the parallelogram OBED is constructed from Z' and $1/\omega C$, the overall impedance Z and phase angle ϕ can be calculated as

$$Z = 686\ \Omega$$

$$\phi = 43^\circ = 0.75 \text{ radians}.$$

(b) The phase angle between current and overall voltage is 43° or 0.75 radians, as derived above.

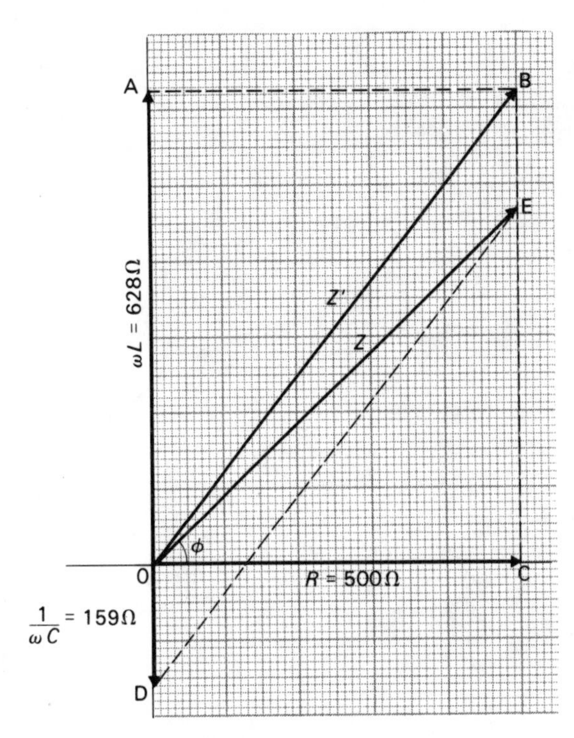

Figure 24 Phasor diagram for SAQ 14

SAQ 15

Because both capacitor and inductor are lossless, the phasors representing their impedances will lie on the y-axis of the phasor diagram.

The impedance of the inductor will be ωL and the impedance of the capacitor will be $1/\omega C$. At resonance, the two impedances are equal in magnitude but opposite in phase.

$$\omega L = \frac{1}{\omega C}$$

$$\omega^2 = \frac{1}{LC},$$

so

$$\omega = \frac{1}{\sqrt{LC}}.$$

SAQ 16

(a) Angular frequency $\omega = 2\pi f$

$= (2\pi \times 200)$ radians s^{-1}

$= 1257$ radians s^{-1}.

Admittance of capacitor $\omega C = (1257 \times 0.5 \times 10^{-6})\,\Omega^{-1}$

$= 6.285 \times 10^{-4}\,\Omega^{-1}$.

Admittance of resistor $\frac{1}{R} = \frac{1}{10^4}$

$= 10^{-4}\,\Omega^{-1}$.

The admittance phasor diagram is shown in Figure 25. Because the parallelogram is a rectangle,

Overall admittance

$= [(1 \times 10^{-4})^2 + (6.285 \times 10^{-4})^2]^{1/2}\,\Omega^{-1}$

$= [(1 + 39.5) \times 10^{8}]^{1/2}\,\Omega^{-1}$

$= 6.4 \times 10^{-4}\,\Omega^{-1}$.

(b) Impedance $= \frac{1}{\text{admittance}}$

$= \frac{1}{6.4 \times 10^{-4}}\,\Omega$

$= 1563\,\Omega$.

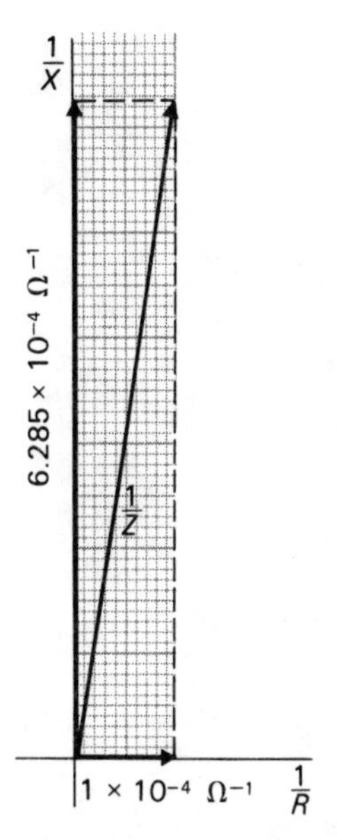

Figure 25 Phasor diagram for SAQ 16

(c) $\tan \phi = \frac{6.285 \times 10^{-4}}{1 \times 10^{-4}}$

$\phi = 81°$

$= 1.4$ radians.

$i = \sin(\omega t + 1.4)$.

SAQ 17

(a) The phasor diagram of current for elements in parallel is illustrated in Figure 20(b) for a capacitance in parallel with a resistance. This could equally well be the phasor diagram of a lossy capacitance, where resistance R represents the loss in the capacitor. So the phasor for the current through a lossy capacitor is in the first quadrant. Similarly the phasor for the current through a lossy inductor is in the fourth quadrant.

(b) A *parallel* arrangement of inductor and capacitor will produce a phasor diagram of current similar to that of Figure 18(b). But whereas the small resultant phasor in Figure 18(b) represents a low impedance for a series arrangement, the small resultant phasor for the parallel arrangement represents a small admittance and therefore a large impedance. So a parallel resonant circuit can be expected to exhibit a larger impedance at the resonant frequency than the impedance of either the inductor or the capacitor on its own.

SAQ 18

Figure 22 can be used to represent the phasor diagram for this question. From Figure 22,

$$\tan \phi = \frac{1/Z_L}{1/R}$$

$$= \frac{R}{Z_L}$$

$$= \frac{R}{\omega L}$$

$$= \frac{500}{2\pi \times 50 \times 2}$$

$$= 0.796.$$

So $\phi = 38.5°$. Power factor is $\cos \phi$, which is $\cos 38.5°$, or 0.78.

UNIT 14: ELECTRICAL INSTRUMENTS

CONTENTS

Aims

The aim of this unit is to demonstrate how the electromagnetic principles of Units 11–13 can be used to design electrical measuring instruments.

Objectives

After studying this unit you should be able to do the following:

1 Define, describe or otherwise explain the terms listed in Table A.

2 Describe the construction of a moving-coil meter and, given the appropriate data, calculate parameters for such a meter.

3 Describe the construction of a modern cathode-ray oscilloscope and outline the function of each of the components in the tube.

4 Calculate the deflection of an electron beam as it passes through the deflector plates of an oscilloscope, given the appropriate data.

Table A Terms introduced in this unit

anode	magnetic shunt
cathode	moving-coil meter
cathode rays	phosphors
cathode-ray oscilloscope	time base
electron gun	

1 INTRODUCTION

1.1 Electrical measurement

Essentially Units 10 to 13 were concerned with describing the behaviour of electrical circuits of different types. Such descriptions are usually expressed in terms of the currents passing through circuit components and the voltages across them. Underlying all of the calculations is the assumption that, if necessary, we can measure these currents and voltages to verify the theory and, indeed, the theories originally arose from such practical measurements.

So, to end this part of the course, this unit is concerned with electrical measuring instruments and it is concerned primarily with two instruments that you will have used at Summer School – the moving-coil meter and the oscilloscope. The intention is to show how such instruments are designed using the theory already developed in Units 10 to 13, so the unit will act as a revision aid to selected parts of the units on electricity and magnetism.

1.2 This week's work

As you will see this is quite a short unit. This is deliberate. If you have not previously studied any electricity and magnetism, the previous four units may well have been rather difficult because of the number of new concepts that were introduced. So when you have completed this unit you should use any spare time to re-read and revise any topics of which you are still unsure and to catch up with any parts of the *Problem Book* that you have had to leave for want of time.

2 THE MOVING-COIL METER

2.1 The principle of the meter

When a current-carrying conductor is placed in a magnetic field, it experiences a force, called the Lorentz force.

SAQ 1 (Revision)

A conductor of length l carries a current I through a field of flux density B. The conductor is at a right angle to the lines of flux.

(a) What is the magnitude of the force experienced by the conductor?

(b) How would you determine the direction of this force?

The existence of the Lorentz force is the basis of the design for an electric motor. If a coil is placed between the poles of a magnet, as shown in Figure 1, then when a current is passed through the coil it will tend to turn in the field.

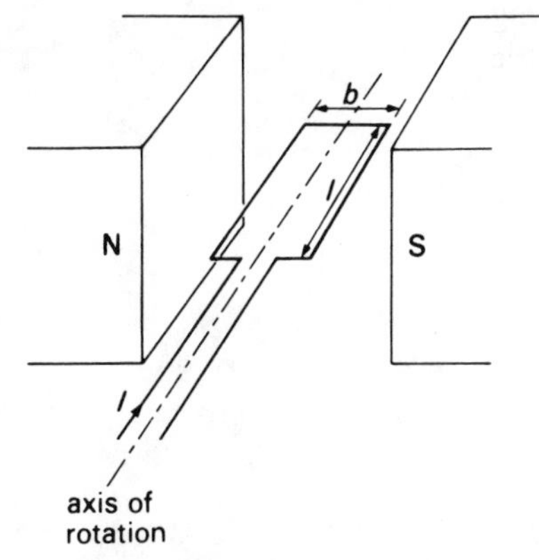

Figure 1 Schematic diagram of a simple electric motor

SAQ 2 (Revision)

A rectangular coil consisting of a single turn of wire of dimensions l and b as shown in Figure 1 carries a current I in the direction shown. It lies between the poles of a large permanent magnet and the flux density B is uniform irrespective of the orientation of the coil. Calculate the following:

(a) The force experienced by the length l of conductor.

(b) The torque experienced by the coil when it lies in the position shown in Figure 1.

(c) The torque experienced by the coil when it has turned through an angle θ from the position shown in Figure 1.

(d) The direction in which the coil will rotate. (Lines of flux are from a north pole to a south pole on a permanent magnet.)

The moving-coil current meter makes use of exactly the same principle as the motor. The essential differences are in the shape of the magnetic field and that, whereas the coil in a motor is allowed to rotate freely, in a moving-coil meter the coil is restrained by a small spring so that the torque produced by the current only causes rotation until it is balanced by the opposing torque of the spring.

2.2 Construction of the meter

Figure 2 shows the construction of a simple moving-coil meter. The magnetic field is provided by a permanent magnet, to which pole pieces of soft magnetic

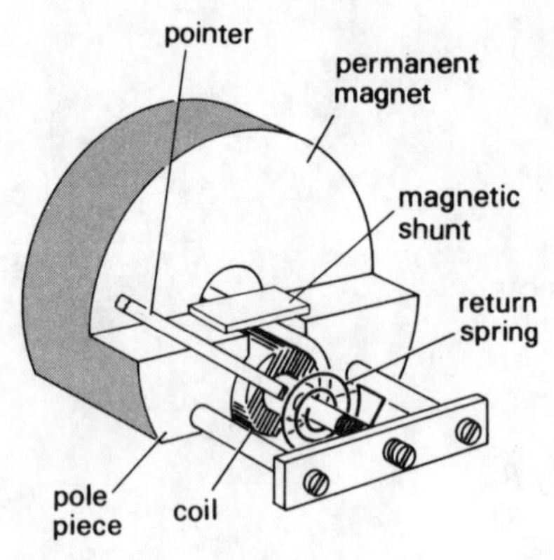

Figure 2 The essential features of a moving-coil meter

material are attached and shaped to ensure that the air gaps are small, as in Figure 3. The iron core of the coil is fixed and is part of the magnetic circuit.

The small coil, through which the current flows, is mounted on a former. The former is free to rotate between two end-stops, except for the return-spring mounted on the shaft. The coil is held in the radial magnetic field so that the field is always perpendicular to the coil. This is shown in Figure 3. The field is

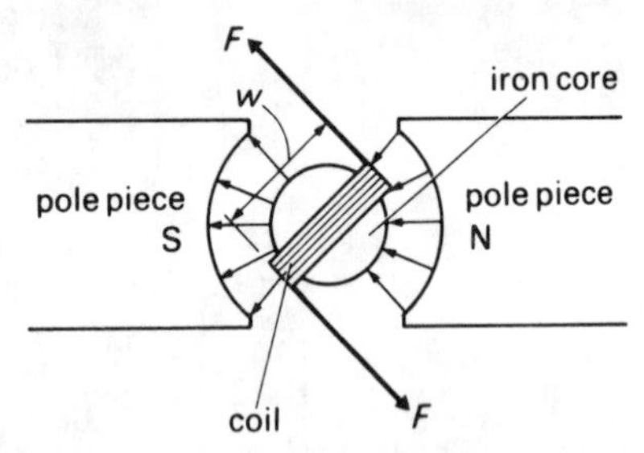

Figure 3 Section through the moving parts of a moving-coil meter

also the same strength everywhere in the gap except at the most extreme orientations of the coil. This means that, for a given current in the coil, the torque exerted by the field on the coil *is the same* whatever the orientation of the coil.

The return-spring is adjusted so that when the current is zero, the coil is at rest with the pointer on the zero-current mark on the scale. For any particular current, the pointer comes to rest when the electromagnetic torque is just balanced by the mechanical torque of the return-spring. The spring is constructed so that the torque exerted by it increases linearly with the angle of deflection. So the pointer deflection is proportional to the current. The rotation of the meter coil is therefore essentially the same as that of a motor coil except that in the meter the coil is restrained by the action of the spring.

Suppose the pointer comes to rest after rotating through an angle θ and suppose the return spring exerts a restoring torque of $k\theta$, where k is a constant for the spring (with units of newton metres per degree). For a coil of area A containing N turns and carrying current I in a field B, the electromagnetic torque is $BNIA$ (see SAQ 2). But in equilibrium these two torques are equal and opposite, so

$$BNIA = k\theta \quad (1)$$

so

$$I = \frac{k}{BNA}\theta \quad (2)$$

In other words, the current I is directly proportional to the deflection θ.

SAQ 3 (Objective 2)

In a particular current meter the return spring exerts a restoring torque of 1.4×10^{-6} N m per degree. The coil in the meter is square, with sides of length 1.5 cm, and has 150 turns. The flux density in the region of the coil is 0.5 T. If the full-scale deflection of the meter corresponds to an angular movement of 120°, what current gives a full-scale deflection?

There are two further points about the design of current meters that are worth noting.

(a) It is, of course, desirable to ensure that the flux density in the annular air gap is, and remains, precisely its intended value (to within the meter accuracy). If this can be achieved then a standard calibration of the meter can be used, and greater economies in manufacture can be achieved. Otherwise meters must be calibrated individually, because the pointer reading for a given current is likely to differ from meter to meter. So, rather than calibrate each meter, it is obviously better, after adjusting the return spring for zero deflection, to adjust the flux density B so that maximum deflection of the pointer coincides with the maximum reading on the scale. The whole meter-scale should then be within specified accuracy.

This adjustment can be achieved by using a *magnetic shunt*. This is a piece of iron that is screwed to one pole piece of the magnet and reaches across the air gap as indicated in Figure 2. It presents a much lower reluctance to the flux than the air gap, and so directs some of the flux away from the gap. By adjusting its position, in particular its area of overlap of the second pole piece, the value of B in the air gap can be easily adjusted.

magnetic shunt

(b) It is very easy to damage current meters by overloading them and thus 'wrapping the pointer round the end-stop'. It is, however, possible to use the speed at which the pointer moves to generate a voltage in a subsidiary coil attached to the main one. This voltage is proportional to the speed of rotation, and so can be used to trip a switch if the pointer moves dangerously fast.

You should now be able to attempt questions 541 to 545 in the *Problem Book*.

---

3 CATHODE-RAY OSCILLOSCOPE

3.1 Cathode rays

It has been known for about three hundred years that gases conduct electricity at low pressures, and while doing so they glow. When vacuum pumps were improved in the last century, it became possible to obtain much lower pressures than had been possible earlier. Since the gas was responsible for conducting the electricity, it might have been expected that its removal to obtain the low pressures would prevent the electric current from flowing. However, at high voltages current continued to flow although the character of the electric current was changed.

The most noticeable change was that the gas no longer glowed but there was a glow from the walls of the tube facing the negative electrode or *cathode*. It was also found that the effect did not depend on the position of the positive electrode or *anode*; for example, the anode could be tucked away in a side tube as

cathode

anode

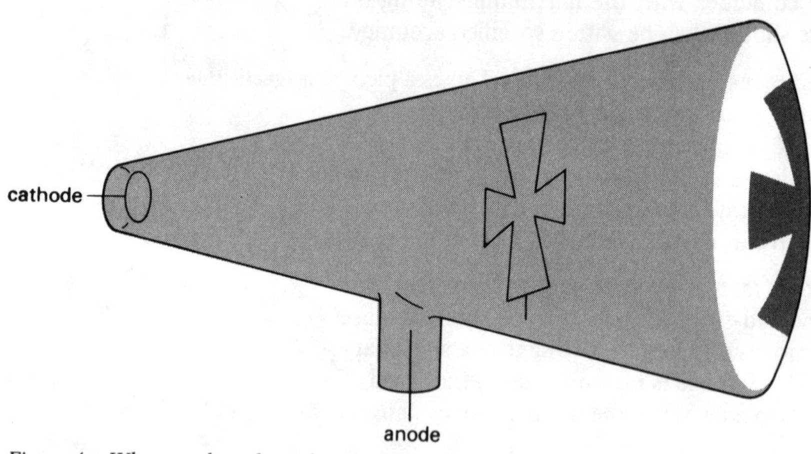

Figure 4 When an obstacle is placed in the path of cathode rays it casts a shadow on the end of the tube facing the cathode. Note how the anode is tucked away in a side tube

shown in Figure 4. Whereas a current through an ordinary conductor, such as a metal or an electrolyte, would proceed directly between the two electrodes, the current in a vacuum tube behaves quite differently.

It was also found that obstacles placed in the tube, such as the cross in Figure 4, would cast a shadow on the end of the tube facing the cathode. It was therefore thought that the glow was caused by rays similar to light rays and, because these rays came from the cathode, they were called *cathode rays*.

cathode rays

Experiments with vacuum tubes revealed several properties of cathode rays, some of which were to be of special importance in identifying the nature of the rays and subsequently in the design of the cathode-ray oscilloscope. For example, it was found that the rays were deflected by electric and magnetic fields, indicating that the rays were charged. From measurements of the deflections produced it was eventually possible to show that they were in fact electrons. Modern cathode-ray oscilloscopes focus the beam and produce deflections using electric and magnetic fields.

Cathode rays also were found to make certain crystals glow very brightly. Such crystals were called *phosphors*. The screens of modern cathode-ray tubes are formed by coating the inside of the glass with a suitable phosphor. Different phosphors glow different colours and so the screen of a colour television is coated with dots of three different phosphors to give the three primary colours.

phosphors

3.2 Early cathode-ray tubes

Cathode-ray tubes were first used to make electrical measurements at the end of the nineteenth century. The idea, which was due to Ferdinand Braun, was to produce a narrow pencil of rays using a low-pressure discharge tube with a mask in front of the cathode and with the end surface coated with a phosphor. This produced a small spot on the screen which would move when the beam was deflected by magnetic coils placed around the outside of the tube. He used this arrangement successfully to make measurements on alternating current.

There are four main problems with a tube of this type.

(a) By using a metal mask to obtain a narrow beam most of the cathode rays generated are lost, so the image on the screen is weak.

(b) Gas discharge tubes need extremely high voltages to operate and so are hazardous as practical instruments.

(c) The gas has to be at an appropriate low pressure and this can be difficult to achieve in a reproducible manner.

(d) When cathode rays are stopped, they cause X-rays to be emitted from the material which stopped them. So such tubes present a potential health hazard.

Modern cathode-ray tubes overcome these problems in a variety of ways. A stream of electrons is generated using a hot cathode, usually a fine tungsten wire coated with a semiconductor and heated by a low voltage source (4–6 V). The electrons are accelerated and focused into a beam by electric fields, and the beam is deflected either by magnetic fields or by further electric fields. The tube is almost completely evacuated so that the electrons seldom collide with gas molecules.

3.3 Modern cathode-ray oscilloscopes

The cathode-ray oscilloscope is a sophisticated electronic measuring instrument, which produces a visual display of the voltage or waveform being investigated. As its name suggests, it uses a cathode-ray tube to produce the visual display.

Figure 5 shows schematically the main components of a modern cathode-ray tube with electrostatic deflection. It is essentially a thick-walled glass tube T, widened at one end to form the screen S. The inner surface of the screen is coated with a suitable phosphor.

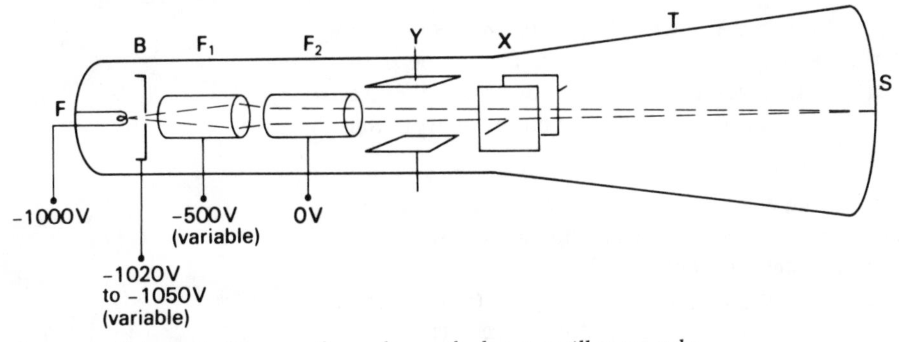

Figure 5 Schematic diagram of a modern cathode-ray oscilloscope tube

Electrons generated by a heated tungsten filament F are attracted by two focusing cylinders F_1 and F_2, maintained at potentials which are positive with respect to the filament. Most of the electrons pass through these cylinders and emerge as a converging beam focused on the screen.

After leaving the focusing cylinders, the beam passes through two pairs of plates, Y and X in Figure 5, to which voltages may be applied from external sources. These deflect the beam.

The brightness of the beam is controlled by electrode B in front of the filament. This is a wire grid. If B is made more negative with respect to the cathode, electrons are repelled so fewer electrons pass through.

The potentials shown in Figure 5 are typical of those used in many commercial instruments. Note that the potentials applied to the brightness grid B and the focusing cylinder F_1 are variable. Also, the final focusing cylinder and the screen are earthed (i.e. at zero potential) for safety. As a consequence the filament is at a high negative potential. The collection of components from filament F_1 through to the final focusing electrode F_2 is often referred to as the *electron gun*.

electron gun

The phosphor screen is also capable of conducting electricity so the electron current is led back to the anode by conduction through the surface coating inside the tube.

3.4 The focusing mechanism

The focusing of the electron beam as it passes through the focusing cylinders F_1 and F_2 in Figure 5 is a good illustration of the theory of electric fields discussed in Unit 11. Let us consider what happens as an electron moves across the gap between them.

Figure 6 shows a section through the cylinders, which we will suppose to be held at potentials of -500 V and 0 V. In the gap a set of equipotentials can be drawn and they will appear as shown with the -250 V equipotential lying midway.

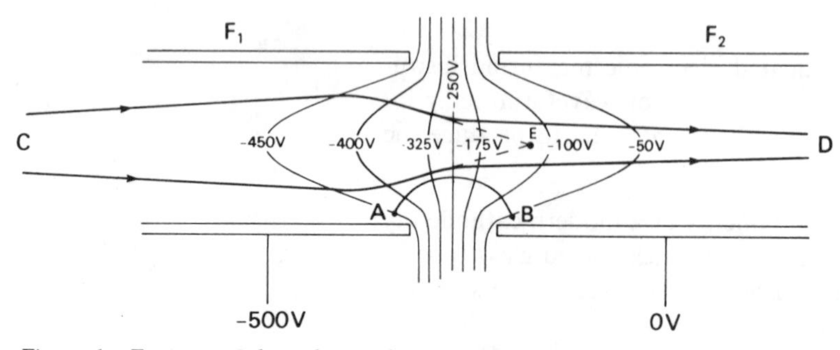

Figure 6 Equipotentials in the gap between focusing electrodes

If a stationary charge were released at point A, it would begin to move so that it crossed the equipotentials at right-angles. It would therefore follow the path AB. That is, in the initial part of its path it would be deflected towards the centre of the tube but in the later part of its trajectory it would be bent away from the centre.

In the oscilloscope tube, however, the electrons are moving at high speed as they approach the gap in the cylinders; they therefore possess considerable momentum. As a result, the electric field merely deflects the beam so that it begins to converge to point E. However, as the electrons pass through the middle of the gap the beam begins to diverge. But since they were accelerated in passing across the gap, the divergence in the second cylinder is less than the convergence in the first cylinder so the net effect is a focusing of the beam as shown by the path CD in Figure 6.

The emergent beam is still somewhat convergent and by careful adjustment of the potentials of the focusing cylinders, the spot on the screen can be made very small – often less than 1 mm in diameter.

3.5 The deflector plates

The oscilloscope is used by applying voltages across the deflector plates (X and Y in Figure 5). These applied voltages set up an electric field between the plates which in turn affects the movement of the electron beam.

To show how the beam is deflected, look at Figure 7. This shows a pair of deflector plates of length D and separation d. Suppose that a voltage V is applied

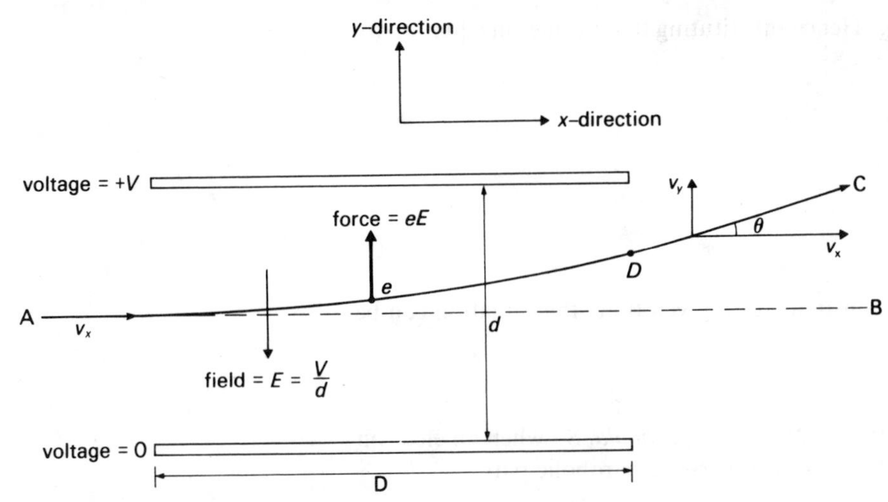

Figure 7 Deflection of an electron in a pair of deflector plates of length D and separation d when a potential V is applied across them

across them. If d is much less than D, the field between the plates will be almost uniform so there will be an electric field E set up between them, where

$$E = \frac{V}{d}. \qquad (3)$$

(We have ignored any fringing effects at the edges of the plates.)

Now suppose that an electron of charge e enters the space between the plates with a velocity v_x which is parallel to the plates, as shown in Figure 7; in other words, if it were not deflected it would continue along the path AB. However, when the field is applied the electron will experience a force of magnitude eE (see Unit 11, section 2) and this will be directed along the lines of electric field; that is, at right angles to the direction of travel, denoted by the y-direction in Figure 7.

This force causes the electron to accelerate at right-angles to the initial direction of motion. But, as we know from Unit 1,

$$\text{Force} = \text{mass} \times \text{acceleration},$$

so

$$eE = ma, \qquad (4)$$

where m is the mass of an electron and a is the acceleration.

Hence, from equations (4) and (3),

$$a = \frac{eE}{m} = \frac{eV}{md}. \qquad (5)$$

If we know the acceleration in the y-direction, then it is a simple task to calculate by how much the beam is deflected in this direction whilst it is between the plates. In Unit 1 one of the equations of motion derived is

$$s = ut + \tfrac{1}{2}at^2, \qquad (6)$$

where

s = distance,
u = initial velocity,
a = acceleration,
t = time.

In this example, the initial velocity in the y-direction is zero, so $u = 0$. The acceleration in the y-direction is given by equation (5). Now suppose that by the time the electron has travelled a distance x in the x-direction, it has been deflected a distance y in the y-direction. The time taken to travel a distance x is simply

$$\frac{\text{Distance}}{\text{Speed}} = \frac{x}{v_x}.$$

So time t in equation (6) is x/v_x. Hence substituting these values in equation (6) gives

$$y = 0 + \frac{1}{2}\frac{eV}{md}\left(\frac{x}{v_x}\right)^2$$

or

$$y = \frac{eV}{2mdv_x^2}x^2. \qquad (7)$$

Since e, V, m, d and v_x are all constants for a given tube, this equation can be written as

$$y = Kx^2,$$

where K is a constant. This is the equation of a *parabola*. So when an electron passes through a constant electric field it traverses a parabolic path.

When the electron has passed through the plates (i.e. reached point D in Figure 7) the total deflection in the y-direction is found by putting $x = D$ in equation (7). Hence

$$\text{Total deflection} = \frac{eVD^2}{2mdv_x^2}. \qquad (8)$$

SAQ 4 (Objective 4)

The deflector plates in an oscilloscope are 1.5 cm long and 3 mm apart. Electrons of velocity 2×10^7 m s^{-1} enter the space between the plates when the applied voltage is 50 V. Calculate the total deflection in the y-direction if the mass of the electron is 9.1×10^{-31} kg and the electron charge is 1.6×10^{-19} C. (You may ignore any fringing at the ends of the plates.)

When the electron leaves the plates it again travels in a straight line but now instead of having just a velocity v_x in the x-direction that it had on entering the

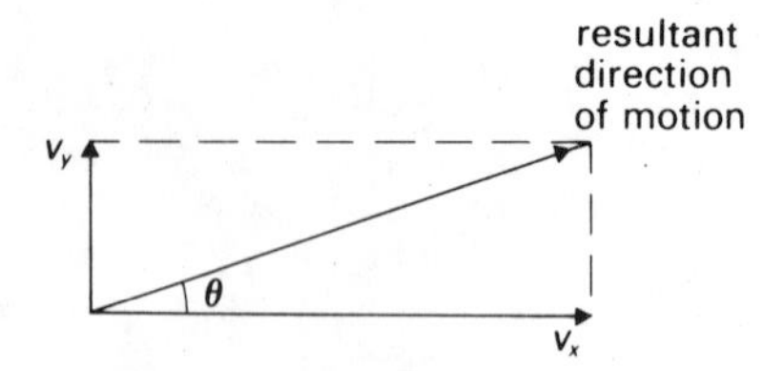

Figure 8 Components of velocity of an electron beam leaving deflector plates

plates, it possesses an additional component v_y in the y-direction as shown in Figure 8. The net result of passing through the plates is therefore an angular deflection θ (see Figures 7 and 8). From Figure 8 it is clear that

$$\tan\theta = \frac{v_y}{v_x}. \qquad (9)$$

But we can calculate a value for v_y because the acceleration while the electron was between the plates is known (equation 5). From the equations of motion in Unit 1 we know that:

$$v = u + at, \qquad (10)$$

where

v = final velocity,

u = initial velocity,

a = acceleration,

t = time.

For motion in the y-direction, $u = 0$, $a = eV/md$ from equation (5), and $t = D/v_x$ (the time the electron spends between the plates). So, using equation (10),

$$v_y = 0 + \frac{eV}{md}\frac{D}{v_x},$$

and substituting this in equation (9) gives:

$$\tan\theta = \frac{eVD}{mdv_x^2}. \qquad (11)$$

This equation is useful in calculating the distance that the spot on the screen

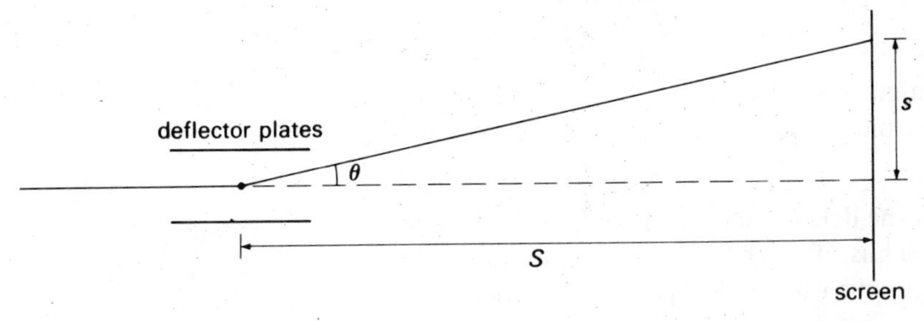

Figure 9 Relation between angular deflection θ of the beam and the distance s moved by the spot on the screen.

will move because, as shown in Figure 9, if s is the distance moved on the screen when the mid-point of the plates is at a distance S from the screen, then

$$\tan\theta = \frac{s}{S}. \qquad (12)$$

SAQ 5 (Objective 4)

(a) Use the data in SAQ 4 to calculate the angular deflection θ of the beam.

(b) If the screen is 200 cm from the middle of the deflector plates calculate the distance the spot on the screen moves when a voltage of 50 V is applied (compared to the position of the spot when no voltage is applied).

3.6 Use of the oscilloscope

If a d.c. source is applied across the deflector plates of an oscilloscope, the spot on the screen is deflected either vertically or horizontally depending on whether the voltage is applied to the X or Y plates in Figure 5.

If an alternating voltage is applied the spot will oscillate between the peak values of the applied voltage. It can also be used to examine the waveform of the applied alternating voltage and this is done by employing a *time base*. Essentially a sawtooth waveform is applied to the X plates. Figure 10 shows such a waveform; during the gradual rise in time t, the spot is swept across the screen. Then during the sudden decrease, the spot flies back to its starting position. Most commercial oscilloscopes have a built-in time base. With the time base switched on, the alternating voltage to be examined is applied to the Y plates to produce a vertical deflection. Thus for a sinusoidal applied voltage, the path

time base

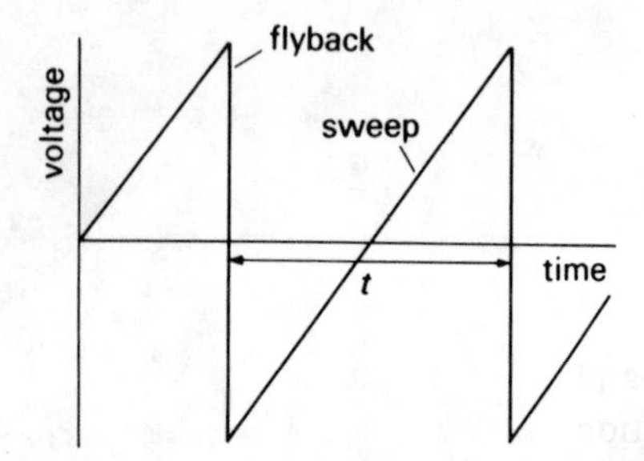

Figure 10 Sawtooth wave such as that used for the time base on an oscilloscope

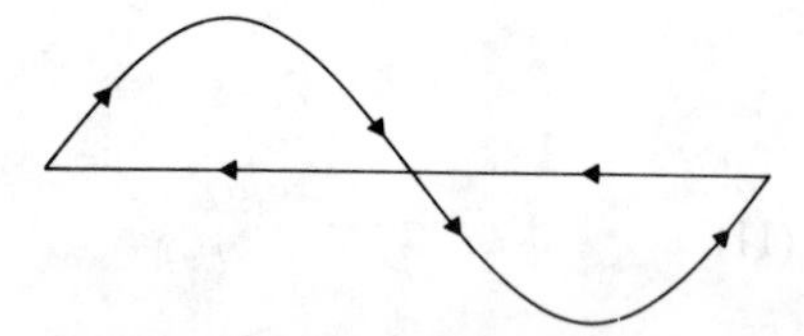

Figure 11 Path traced out by the spot on an oscilloscope screen when a sinusoidal alternating voltage is applied to the Y plates and a sawtooth time base, such as that shown in Figure 10, is applied to the X plates

traced out by the spot on the screen might appear as shown in Figure 11. In this case, the time for one cycle of the sinusoid is equal to the time t of the sweep of the time base.

From equation (8) it can be seen that the deflection of the spot is proportional to the voltage applied to the plates. Thus, if the oscilloscope is suitably calibrated, the amplitude of the voltage applied to the Y plates can be measured by measuring the amplitude of the waveform traced out on the screen.

The great advantage of the oscilloscope as an electrical measuring instrument is its almost instantaneous response to any applied signal. For this reason it is widely used in many diverse applications.

You should now be able to attempt questions 546 to 550 in the *Problem Book*.

---

4 POSTSCRIPT

You have now reached the end of the block of units concerned with electricity and magnetism, so if you encounter the topics dealt with here in any future courses you should have a good foundation on which to build. As noted at the beginning of this unit, this unit is intentionally short so you should spend any remaining time this week revising any topics that you found particularly difficult and catching up on the *Problem Book*.

ANSWERS TO SELF-ASSESSMENT QUESTIONS

SAQ 1

This is revision of the Lorentz force, as described in Unit 12.

(a) The force F experienced by a conductor of length l which carries a current I through a magnetic field of flux density B is given by

$$F = BIl \sin \theta,$$

where θ is the angle between the conductor and the lines of flux. If, as in the question, the conductor is perpendicular to the lines of flux,

$$\theta = 90^\circ$$
$$\sin \theta = 1,$$

so

$$F = BIl$$

(b) The direction of the force is given by Fleming's left-hand motor rule (see Unit 12); that is

First finger points along field.
Second finger points along current.
Thumb points in direction of force.

SAQ 2

This is revision of the electric-motor principles given in Unit 12.

(a) The force F experienced by the conductor of length l carrying current I in a field B is, as in SAQ 1,

$$F = BIl.$$

Note the angle term $\sin \theta$ does not come into this expression because the conductor is always at right angles to the lines of flux.

(b) The torque is the product of force and the perpendicular distance of the line of action of the force from the axis of rotation. In the position shown in Figure 1, the force on one side of the coil is BIl and the perpendicular distance from the axis of rotation is $b/2$. So torque due to this single force is $BIlb/2$. But there is a second force on the other side of the coil, so the total torque is double this value; that is, $BIlb$ or BIA, where A is the area of the coil.

(c) When the coil rotates, the distance between the line of action of the force and the axis of rotation *decreases*. After a rotation θ from the position shown in Figure 1, the distance is no longer $b/2$ but $(b \sin \theta)/2$. So the total torque is $BIlb \sin \theta$ or $BIA \sin \theta$. (Note that if the coil had N turns the torque would be $BNIA \sin \theta$.)

(d) Application of Fleming's left-hand rule shows that the left-hand side of the coil will move down. In other words the coil will start to rotate in an anticlockwise direction.

SAQ 3

This is a straightforward application of equation (1), i.e.

$$NBIA = k\theta,$$

where

$$B = 0.5\ \text{T},$$
$$A = (1.5 \times 1.5)\ \text{cm}^2 = (0.015 \times 0.015)\ \text{m}^2 = 2.25 \times 10^{-4}\ \text{m}^2,$$
$$k = 1.4 \times 10^{-6}\ \text{N m degree}^{-1},$$
$$N = 150\ \text{turns},$$
$$\theta = 120^\circ.$$

Equation (1) can be rearranged to give

$$I = \frac{k\theta}{NBA} = \frac{1.4 \times 10^{-6} \times 120}{150 \times 0.5 \times 2.25 \times 10^{-4}}\ \text{A} = 0.010\ \text{A} = 10\ \text{mA}.$$

SAQ 4

This is a straightforward application of equation (8), where:

$$e = 1.6 \times 10^{-19}\ \text{C},$$
$$V = 50\ \text{V},$$
$$D = 1.5\ \text{cm} = 0.015\ \text{m},$$
$$m = 9.1 \times 10^{-31}\ \text{kg},$$
$$d = 3\ \text{mm} = 0.003\ \text{m},$$
$$v_x = 2 \times 10^7\ \text{m s}^{-1}.$$

$$\text{Deflection} = \frac{eVD^2}{2mdv_x^2} = \frac{1.6 \times 10^{-19} \times 50 \times 0.015^2}{2 \times 9.1 \times 10^{-31} \times 0.003 \times (2 \times 10^7)^2}\ \text{m} = 0.0008\ \text{m} = 0.8\ \text{mm}.$$

SAQ 5

(a) This is a straightforward application of equation (11), where

$$e = 1.6 \times 10^{-19}\ \text{C},$$
$$V = 50\ \text{V},$$
$$D = 1.5\ \text{cm} = 0.015\ \text{m},$$
$$m = 9.1 \times 10^{-31}\ \text{kg},$$
$$d = 3\ \text{mm} = 0.003\ \text{m},$$
$$v_x = 2 \times 10^7\ \text{m s}^{-1}.$$

So

$$\tan \theta = \frac{eVD}{mdv_x^2} = \frac{1.6 \times 10^{-19} \times 50 \times 0.015}{9.1 \times 10^{-31} \times 0.003 \times (2 \times 10^7)^2} = 0.11.$$

Hence

$$\theta = 6.3^\circ.$$

(b) $$\text{Tan}\ \theta = \frac{\text{deflection on screen}}{\text{distance from middle of plates to screen}} = \frac{s}{S}\ \text{(see equation 12).}$$

$$s = S \tan \theta = 0.022\ \text{m} = 2.2\ \text{cm}.$$

T281 BASIC PHYSICAL SCIENCE FOR TECHNOLOGY

Unit 1: Motion, Newton's laws and friction

Unit 2: Work, energy, density and pressure

Unit 3: Further properties of matter

Unit 4: Heat and thermodynamics I

Unit 5: Heat and thermodynamics II

Unit 6: Introductory chemistry

Unit 7: Equilibrium

Unit 8: Rate

Unit 9: Thermochemistry

Unit 10: Electricity

Unit 11: Electromagnetics I

Unit 12: Electromagnetics II

Unit 13: Alternating current

Unit 14: Electrical instruments

Unit 15: Waves

Unit 16: Geometrical optics